# About the Author

I've been a sign writer and artist since 1982. Prior to that, I possibly hold the record for the number of full-time jobs that anyone can have. In sixteen years, I've held down twenty or more! This has, however, furnished me with many, often amusing, true stories, some of which are revealed in this, my first book.

Art, in all of its manifestations, is both my hobby and my trade. The accompanying illustrations are my own work and I hope they bring these tales to life.

Phil Kershaw.

# The Petrol Fairy and Other True Stories

**Phil Kershaw**

# The Petrol Fairy and Other True Stories

Olympia Publishers
*London*

**www.olympiapublishers.com**
OLYMPIA PAPERBACK EDITION



A CIP catalogue record for this title is
available from the British Library.

ISBN: 978-1-80074-077-8


First Published in 2021

Olympia Publishers
Tallis House
2 Tallis Street
London
EC4Y 0AB
Printed in Great Britain

## Dedication

In loving memory of my dear wife, Jill, 1948 — 2017.

# Introduction

I have collected these stories over the last fifty years or so, religiously writing them down as they occurred or were disclosed to me, so they would not be forgotten. My many varied careers before settling down as a sign writer and artist, have led me to encounter some interesting subject matter. I have sketched the accompanying illustrations under the pen name 'Gadge'.

One man's tragedy is sometimes the cause of another's mirth. I was often presented with the great difficulty of having to listen carefully, feigning deep concern on the outside, to some woeful tale, whilst chortling away quietly on the inside.

I am deeply indebted to the many friends, relatives and acquaintances who have contributed their 'Nuggets', often quite embarrassing, some possibly illegal but none the less, amusing accounts from their own experiences.

Although I have kept as close to the original true stories as possible, I have added embellishments to create suspense and jeopardy. Some names and locations have been changed, 'to protect the innocent. And more importantly, the guilty!'

'The Miller's Arms' was indeed the scene of many disclosures and some action. In addition, I have set the telling of some other tales here, as a useful vehicle, introducing a 'Story Teller's Chair' as a platform.

# Jolly Roger

It was Pete Fuller who started what we called 'The Jolly Roger Fan Club' at The Miller's Arms. A few of the pub's regulars were well heeled and would always listen to 'investment advice'. Pete was perhaps the most affluent among us, having made a huge fortune flogging suspension parts to the motor industry; so when he gave a tip, lots listened. A true 'regular', indeed if you walked in and Pete wasn't propping up the bar, you'd think you were at the wrong pub. Always smartly turned out in a light sports jacket and chinos, Pete had lots of 'connections', some of whom you definitely wouldn't invite to your New Year's Eve bash. An eager audience of pseudo-affluent barflies hung onto his every word…

"I got my original twenty grand investment back from Jolly Roger today, with an additional four grand of interest, after only three months! That's twenty percent!" announced Pete to all and sundry in the bar, one rainy Friday night in August 1976. "I challenge anyone to beat that as an investment!" He scanned the assemblage seeking gratification. None came.

"But I heard he only deals in cash or cheques, ain't that a bit dodgy, Pete?" asked our Cockney ex-taxi driver, Chips. His own modest 'nest egg', he had already decided, was staying exactly where it was, safe and sound in Berkley's Bank's vault, thank you very much. Stockily built with a somewhat prehensile, strawberry-shaped nose, 'Chips' was not his given name and it was best not to ask.

"That's no problem for me, Chippy." Pete knew he'd made Chips wince without even looking at him.

"It's 'Chips', thank you! Chips is me moniker. And I ain't no bloody carpenter! Leave out the 'Pee' Pete!"

"…cash is no problem," continued Pete, ignoring Chips' indignation. "If a trader wants cash, I draw some out. Simple. Anyway, I'll be re-investing again with Roger, first thing on Monday morning."

"Where's his office, Pete?" asked Big Julie, "I might put a few bob in, myself." Julie was second to Pete as far as bar attendance went and for a very good reason. She rented the pub's only lettable room and had merely to roll out of bed and ease her robust frame swiftly down the pub's stairs. Julie's stool at the far left of the bar was exclusive, nobody else ever sat on it. A natural blonde, but with some 'bottled help' these days, Big Julie was affable enough, again, with some 'bottled help'.

"On Jury Street, just past the jeweller's, on the same side. Large, double width door with 'Jolly Roger Investments' on a brass plate. Can't miss it. Come to think of it, you can't miss him!" replied Pete.

"I hear he's a huge chap?" asked Bill the landlord, pulling a pint of 'Yore Inn', the pub's own brew cask ale. Bill had his name above the pub's front door. 'William Waterman, licensed purveyor of Wines, Ales

Spirits & Tobacco' proclaimed the sign. But all 'Milly' regulars knew very well that it was in fact Bill's wife Caroline, or 'Kaz' who actually ran the pub and wore the trousers. Kaz was quite a character though and could be quite formidable.

"Oh yes, he's a mountain of a man. Likes his grub! Mind you, he can afford it! Would you like me to introduce you to him on Monday morning, Julie?" asked Pete.

"Oh yes please Pete, shall we meet, say around ten a.m., at the Abbotsford Coffee Shop, opposite Jolly Roger's?' Seeing Pete nod 'yes' she turned to Chips, "Can I have a taxi to Jury Street with you on Monday morning around nine forty-five please me old mate?" Chips gave a 'thumbs up" mid swig. A little 'cash job' was always welcome. Just don't mention it to Henry, who worked at the Inland Revenue. Looking round, he was relieved to see that the pub's very own sandy-haired young 'Tax Advisor' wasn't present.

"I'll be there," said Pete, emptying his glass. "Same again please, Bill, and one for Julie. And I suppose you can just about manage a half, can you, Chips?" He winked at the landlord.

"A ha-ha-ha-half!" spluttered Chips, swiftly emptying his glass. "I can't even pronounce the bloody word. Make mine a pint. Ta."

Pete held open the extra-wide door as he and Julie entered Roger Stornaway's office on Monday morning. Julie was shocked at the sheer size of Roger. She herself was 'large', but this huge specimen was literally 'taking the biscuit'! Or rather a barrel of them! Roger 'sprawled' rather than sat, on what she guessed must have been a reinforced chair, behind a generous desk piled with paperwork, calculators and tinned sweets.

He was dressed in a bespoke striped, grey suit, with a hell of a lot more stripes than suited the suit. Alarmingly, the buttons on his over-stretched waistcoat looked about to be launched as missiles. A white bow tie with red spots was trying its best at strangulation. His wide head was topped by a wild mop of black hair. Wedge-shaped sideburns seemed to add even more width. Bright blue sparkling eyes gleamed out from under bushy brows and through large, rectangular spectacles. He had an intelligent, friendly look about him, Julie thought. But oh dear, he did look a tad 'sweaty'. A fan whirring away nearby seemed to be having little effect.

"Good morning Pete, good to see you again, and who's this lovely lady? Your daughter?" asked the huge man, jovially. He somehow managed to rise quite unexpectedly quickly from his seat, revealing a huge stuffed giant panda mascot sitting behind him, next to a skull and crossbones flag. The walls were decorated with a collection of share performance charts, variously labelled 'RR', 'ICI', 'Courtaulds' etc. Julie noticed that they all appeared to show very positive climbing trend lines, rising from left to right. Things were looking good.

"Roger, this is my friend Julie. Julie, this is Roger Stornaway, of Jolly Roger Investments," announced Pete, wafting his hand in the general direction of the fat futures expert.

As Julie locked eyes and shook hands with Roger, she noted a new moistness in her palm.

"Sweet?" Roger invited the pair to take a Quality Street or two from a half-full tin. Roger did not take a sweet himself. He hadn't consumed any sugar for ten years.

"Pleased to meet you Roger, I've been hearing a lot about you!" declared the big lass, helping herself to two of the purple treats, which happened to be her favourites.

"And there's a lot of me to hear about!" joked the man mountain. "What can I do for you this morning, Julie?" Roger mopped his brow with a red paisley silk handkerchief. Yes, he did sweat a hell of a lot, Julie noticed. Perhaps it was a glandular problem, she thought.

"I'd like to place an investment with you please Roger, if five thousand pounds isn't too small a sum?" she asked. "Pete has already told me about your 'Share Scheme'. Is it correct, that you do the choosing as to which companies to invest our money in, saving us that chore?"

"That's absolutely correct Julie, and thank you for clarifying those points, Pete. Stocks and shares are so volatile, constantly changing, so to get the very best results we need to move funds rapidly. At the moment we are enjoying a 'Bull' market in many stock exchanges worldwide. Here at Jolly Roger, we constantly track share prices so that we can exploit this fully and importantly swiftly, maximising profits. And of course, no sum is too small, I've even had schoolchildren in here investing their pocket money, bless them!" said Roger proudly, as he filled in a form for Julie and took her cheque.

"There is no minimum term for our 'Portfolio Investment Shares Scheme', and you can withdraw your money any time you like!" The big man beamed as he handed Julie her receipt. "Now, Pete, my dear friend, how can I help you this morning?"

Pete placed a huge stack of notes on the desk. "Here's fifty grand, Roger. Could you invest this for me in your excellent Shares Scheme?" You bet Roger could, and did. Gleefully.

The two customers left Jolly Roger's that Monday morning feeling very pleased with themselves. In twenty minutes, they'd spent fifty-five grand between them, in exchange for four toffees. At £13,750 each, probably the most expensive toffees ever.

During the 1970s Jolly Roger Investments experienced a boom. Word soon got around that withdrawals were always paid back promptly, at any time, no questions asked, and with a very generous amount of interest added. Good news to all with spare cash. Good news that spread like wildfire through the close-knit community of Warwick. This was surely the obvious place to put your money? Most withdrawals were swiftly returned to Roger, to be reinvested in his P.I.S.S. fund, usually in much larger amounts. Warwick mattresses sagged. Roger Stornaway's safe swelled, as did his belly. Apparently.

"Can I invest a hundred thousand pounds?" asked Todd Brown, a well-to-do, well-built builder from Welford one fine Thursday morning, three weeks later. "Hope you don't mind it all in Scottish fifty pound notes though, Roger?"

The stockbroker noticed the shovel-sized hands of the muscular, blonde haired builder as he opened a case and proceeded to build an enormous stack of banknotes on his desk. Todd had made a successful living in the building trade, mostly by fair means, but occasionally foul. Today's investment represented numerous 'Brown Envelope' cash jobs and this was a 'follow up', having benefitted from a previous visit to Roger. Although this would be a large amount of money to most, this was mere 'chicken feed' to Todd. Not a character you'd want to cross though, he looked quite a 'bruiser' thought Roger.

"Scottish notes are legal tender, so no problem at all Todd, and thank you for choosing Jolly Roger again for your investment!" The stockbroker then proceeded to load Todd's 'investment' into his counting machine and on confirming the amount, issued a receipt. "Due to the present buoyancy of the stock market, we are currently paying out at around twenty percent interest over a three-month span. But if you wish to withdraw your money earlier, that's fine." The shares expert smiled warmly while reciting this well-rehearsed mantra. A mantra that he would never utter again. Complete and utter twaddle, thought Roger, to himself.

As he emerged from the wide boy's office into the bright sunlight that early September morning, a hundred thousand pounds lighter, Todd Brown of T. Brown Builders had absolutely no idea.

No idea that the advice to reinvest from his mate Sam, who drank regularly in The Miller's Arms, would prove to be so bad.

No idea that he would not see his money again.

No idea that he would be the very last person ever to see the scheming fat Roger Stornaway.

No idea that he would soon spend a lot of time being interviewed, first by the police, then later by the media, then by the Inland Revenue.

Pete Fuller very nearly choked to death on his bacon sandwich when the headline HUNT FOR 'JOLLY ROGER', screamed at him from the front page of The Warwick Express a week later, at breakfast in his conservatory.

After his attractive, slim, brunette wife Jane patted him vigorously and very hard — too hard? — on the back, he eventually recovered his breathing and read on….

'Investment banker disappears with huge haul of cash…' 'Customers left high and dry…' 'Full-scale manhunt underway…' 'Public asked to be on the lookout for the unmistakeable thirty-five stone fugitive…' A half-page photograph of the familiar wide boy, smiling mockingly back at him from page two confirmed Pete's worst fears.

"Bastard!" Pete managed to splutter between deep breaths, "so it was all a big swindle after all!" His face was gradually turning pink again Jane noticed. It had been purple at one stage.

"I did think," said Jane, "when you first told me about the huge interest he was giving, 'this seems too good to be true'."

"You didn't think to warn me though…?" Pete knew what the reply would be.

"Waste of time. You'd made up your mind and experience has taught me that trying to convince you otherwise is absolutely futile. Always has been. Always will be." Jane knew she was right. Pete knew she was right.

"But he was so convincing… when I asked for my twenty grand back he didn't bat an eyelid, he simply looked at some files marked 'ICI' 'Philip Morris' and 'Coca Cola' and worked out on a calculator that I was due interest at twenty per cent. He opened his safe and took out twenty-four grand and handed it over. Of course, I went straight back with a lot more cash to invest as soon as I could…"

"And you said you'd recommended him to your mates at The Milly?"

"Oh God, I know of at least ten punters from there who've now lost their money. Oh God… Big Julie'll kill me!"

Pete took his wife Jane's advice and steered well clear of the Miller's Arms that night. In fact, he never again crossed the threshold of our favourite pub. He stopped taking phone calls altogether and he soon moved away from his extensive Leamington Spa house to live in Coventry.

"That fat scoundrel!" shouted Big Julie to all and sundry that night, causing some alarm amongst The Milly's bar cronies, "He stole five grand from me! And I'll bet that Sue, my little Shih Tzu, knows a fat lot more about stocks and shares than that fat bastard does! And as for Pete and his bloody stupid investment tips, just wait til I get my hands on him!" We'd never seen her so furious. We were equally shocked at the appalling choice of name for her dog.

"I did try to warn you off him, Julie," reminded Chips with merriment in his voice, smiling so much that his 'strawberry' nose 'nose-dived' down to almost meet his top lip, "but you just wouldn't listen!" The Cockney shook his head mockingly. "My money's still safe and sound in the bank by the way. I reckon you lot." he pointed towards the group of sad-looking investors busy drowning their sorrows, "have been well and truly… errr… 'Rogered'!" he guffawed. This remark was met with roars of laughter, but only from non-investors.

Chips promised himself that he would 'feast' on this theme, with relish, for many years to come.

Two weeks later, my pal, the mischievous mechanic Ivan 'The Terrible', popped into the Milly's bar. He announced, very loudly to the startled customers: "Jolly Roger found!" All barflies hushed immediately and heads swivelled. "Jolly Roger found," he continued, "plenty of gullible fools in Warwick!" He finished and left abruptly, ducking a deftly-aimed beer mat.

As soon as Todd Brown left after making his one hundred-thousand-pound investment that sunny Thursday morning, indeed the very instant this very last 'client' closed the door, Roger sprang into action. He leapt from his reinforced chair, bolted over and bolted the double-width door, then he drew the velvet curtains. Anyone watching would not have believed how fast such a mountain of a man could move, when the need arose.

Roger then began a metamorphosis akin to that of a caterpillar into a butterfly. First, he removed the black wig to reveal a rather feeble sandy-grey comb-over. Then off came the sideburns, revealing a surprisingly slim, clean-shaven, hatchet face. Next to go was the huge foam-padded striped, grey suit jacket and waistcoat, followed by the vast padded trousers. The bow tie and XXXL shirt were next. The newly slimmed-down Roger then stepped into a pair of thirty-two inch waist blue drainpipe jeans and pulled on a medium-sized bright multi-coloured Hawaiian shirt that the fat Roger could have worn only in his wildest dreams. Only underwear and sandals remained from his earlier outfit. A straw boater and Foster Grant sunglasses completed the new look.

The slim man then emptied the safe. When added to Todd Brown's still warm recent kind donation, the haul totalled just over one and a half million pounds sterling. 'Sterling effort!' thought Roger, as a wry smile crossed his face. He stuffed a large suitcase with the money, the wig, sideburns and the old 'fat' padded clothing. There

Julie was shocked at the sheer size of Roger.

was no room for Preston the giant panda so he was left to face the music alone, when the police broke the door down five days later after an anonymous tip off.

Two minutes later, a svelte and dapper-looking tourist carrying a suitcase emerged from the office's rear door, loaded his luggage and climbed into a brand-new bright yellow Austin Mini Clubman. He started the engine and drove out of the car park. He turned right at the one-way sign and swanned off down Swan Street. Here, he stopped at a zebra crossing to allow a well-built gentleman to cross the road.

Midway across the road Todd Brown turned his head, smiled and waved a friendly 'thank you' towards the driver of the yellow car. Then he stopped. His jaw dropped. The driver's face seemed very familiar. Uncannily familiar. Their eyes met. The driver smiled awkwardly back, with a sort of twisted grin. But Todd couldn't place the face, probably because it was 'out of context' he'd thought, or was he completely mistaken? The builder scratched his head, continued crossing and the car roared off.

To this day, nobody knows where Roger Stornaway went after that. Many people would have liked to have known. Some still do.

Undoubtedly, amongst the many swindled investors there was a certain element who would not have ruled out some sort of physical retribution. Some say Roger may have ended up in a 'supporting role', quite literally supporting a bridge over the M42 motorway, which was under construction at that time. But there is no concrete evidence.

UPDATE REPORT: Forty-five years later I can report that there is no update to report.

Footnote: At least our lesser-known Warwick Ponzi Schemer made off with his ill-gotten gains; whereas the famous Bernie Madoff didn't do as his surname suggested and was apprehended and sentenced to a one hundred and fifty year prison term in the U.S.

# Miracle Mince

During the nineteen eighties I was Warwick's local Sign Writer, so I got to know landlord Bill and his wife Kaz quite well and occasionally I wrote signs for The Miller's Arms. This ended up to mutual benefit, as the fifteenth century oak-beamed pub became my 'local' for many years.

On one occasion, my jokey nature got me into trouble, though.

Caroline, or Kaz as she preferred to be called, the slim, forty-something, mousey-haired wife of Bill 'The Landlord', was the pub's actual boss, contrary to what I'd written on the licensee sign over their door.

Two days after writing some menu item updates on the pub's blackboards, I was accosted by Kaz on entering the bar. "What on Earth were you thinking of, Phil?" She sounded very annoyed.

She pointed to the blackboards, on which I'd written:

**'Scampi and Chips in the Basket, £5.95'**

**'Chicken and Chips in the Basket £5.95'**

**'Fishcakes and Chips in the Basket £4.95'.** Underneath these items there was still space for me to write a naughty little 'extra', so I'd written, in the same neat font:

**'Soup in the Basket £2.25'**.

To me it was obviously a joke. But not to Kaz. "You bloody idiot, we've had loads of people asking for 'Soup in the Basket!'" she said angrily.

Anyway, I consoled her and agreed to pop in the next day to rectify the board. Some folk just haven't got a sense of humour!

A little later I decided to entertain the throng of regulars by sitting in The Story Teller's Chair.

Many of the pub's customers have claimed to have come up with the original idea; to have a 'special' chair, placed near the fireplace, from which an occupant could tell a humorous, but essentially true, story. The jury's out on who it was.

An audience of around thirty souls assembled in the bar as I sat down and started my story:

As some of you might be aware, I've had a few jobs in my time, before settling on sign writing. During the nineteen sixties I worked as a 'Butcher's Boy' for Fred Frogley, a suitably rotund and rosy-cheeked butcher. Fred had a corner shop in Kenilworth. A dapper chap, always well turned out in a crisply ironed white smock and trilby. He was in most ways a pillar of the community. Fred, however, had some, err, let's say 'unusual' methods...

'F. Frogley: High Class Family Butcher' proclaimed the shop's fascia sign. I've always thought that 'High Class Family Butcher', a commonly used phrase since the nineteenth century, could be misinterpreted. It sounded rather sinister to me. Beware if you have a high class family?

Sited on a main road in Kenilworth, the shop had a good turnover with mostly local customers. Home delivery became my main job and I rode the unwieldy single-geared bike laden with meat speedily enough, especially when being chased by hungry dogs! It was such a relief though, when I passed my driving test and drove the van instead.

In butchery, as with many trades, there are certain 'tricks'. Wary customers would often ask for 'six sausages' rather than 'half a pound', preventing the usual response, 'Oh, it's just over, is that okay, madam?' This apparent inability to judge exact weights seemed to be endemic. Another often used ruse was to rest a finger on the scales to add weight. Fred must have sold his little finger so many times it was literally worth its weight in gold!

But Fred's main earner, his 'piece de resistance' was undoubtedly his high-level minced meat recycling trick.

The shop's mincing machine was positioned deliberately very high on the back counter. So high in fact that unless they were at least seven feet tall, customers could not see into the top tray. This was for a very good reason. Lurking in this tray, ready to be incorporated into mince, were various odd bits, off-cuts, offal, gristle, fat, etc., which could be secretly added to the customer's original choice of meat. This was an 'economical' way of using up what would otherwise have been discarded. A low step was placed adjacent to the mincer to enable staff to reach and see into the tray.

When weighing 'recycled' mince, I noticed Fred

would kindly refrain from resting his little finger on the scales and I have even seen him give slightly overweight of this 'recycled' product!

As the well-dressed, glamorous looking American lady entered the shop, Fred doffed his pristine white trilby. "G'morning ma'am," he gushed, "what can I do for you today?" This was a ritual every Saturday. It was rare that Woody, Fred's balding, middle-aged, second in command, or myself as a trainee, would be allowed to serve this lady. She was undoubtedly Fred's most treasured customer.

"Good morning Fred, I'd like five pounds of fillet steak, please, we're having family and friends round for a barbecue this afternoon!" she drawled.

Fred beamed, sharpened his knife and offered it to the most expensive cut in the shop, proceeding to cut the usual inch and a half thick steaks.

"Oh, no, I'd like it minced, please Fred, not cut into steaks, you see I'm gonna make hamburgers with it!"

The colour drained from the Master Butcher's usually ruddy cheeks. "Hamburgers?" he squeaked, so incredulous as to momentarily lose control of his voice. He transferred five pounds of the undercut to the mincing machine's top tray. It was an unusual request, to have the Holy Grail of steaks minced; sacrilege even, some would say.

But the butcher's smile gradually reappeared as he hopped up onto the step and switched the machine on. Fred was relieved to see that there was a good amount of 'donor meat' already waiting that morning in the tray.

Firstly he did indeed reluctantly feed a small piece of genuine fillet steak into the blades. But only a small slither, closely followed by all the other 'odds and sods' in the tray. Amongst other motley pieces of 'meat' awaiting incorporation that day, there was an old almost black piece of brisket, some pork fat, half an ox cheek, some chicken giblets and a lamb's spleen.

Fred minced the right weight, or slightly more, of mainly offal and off-cuts, leaving the majority of the precious fillet steak un-minced and importantly re-saleable, still hidden in the machine's top tray. The colour of the mince was a bit streaky as it left the machine, but Fred deftly blended the mince with his hand in the collection bowl, making it a uniform and presentable dark pink. A work of art. The American lady duly paid and left the shop with five pounds of what we considered to be very expensive dog meat.

As soon as the American lady left the shop, Fred proudly showed Woody and me the amount of fillet he had saved by his misdeed. Yes, it was most of it. Probably about half my wages for that week was generated by this fiddle.

Fred boasted of his achievement all week long. "That's the way to make money!" he reminded us constantly… He even took to bursting into song at odd moments when the shop was empty, '*Ooooh yoooo gotta pick a pocket or twoooo'*… from Oliver Twist, and Paul Young's '*Every time you go away, you take a piece of meat with you'* were his favourites. He hadn't got a bad voice actually and me and Woody occasionally joined in, much to Fred's delight.

We'd break off mid song if a customer entered, but one chap said, "Oh no, don't stop for me, please continue, I love a good old sing-song!" and he even joined in!

For that one happy week, working at Frogley's High Class Family Butchers was sheer bliss; akin to starring in our own Broadway musical. All good things though don't last for ever. Then came another Saturday. An extraordinary Saturday. A Saturday I've never forgotten…

Fred seemed a little subdued that morning. Perhaps he was anticipating something? Oh yes!

At the very instant the doorbell 'dinged' and the American lady entered the shop on that following Saturday morning, Fred was already halfway out of the back door. The speed achievable by such a portly chap astonished us. But the lady had spotted him, calling him back to the counter.

"Fred, Fred, hi, Fred, can I please speak to you about that minced fillet steak you sold me last week?" Her drawl reached a high, catlike screech.

Woody winked at me and nodded his head towards the American lady as if to say 'You don't want to miss this!' Indeed, we were a lot more attentive than usual… we wouldn't have missed this for the world!

Sheepishly, the master butcher turned and slowly approached the counter, without the usual jaunty spring in his step. "G'morning, ma'am," he tried to sound upbeat, but we could hear his voice quavering.

"Fred, do you remember that fillet steak you minced for me last Saturday, for our barbecue?" asked the American lady.

"Yes," Fred squeaked feebly. Of course he'd remembered it! Woody and I dared not even look at each other at this stage, for fear of corpsing into guffaws of hysteria.

There was a pregnant pause that seemed to go on for aeons…

"I made some hamburgers with it."

Fred visibly decreased in size, "Ah… yes, I remember," he managed, in a high-pitched squeak. "How were they?" Even Fred couldn't believe he was actually asking this question.

"The Mayor of Kenilworth and some Town Councillors and other dignitaries were among my guests. Everyone there had at least one of those hamburgers each."

Fred gulped. "At least one?" Woody and me stared open mouthed at each other. Fred seemed very subdued. We hadn't seen him like this before.

"Some had a lot more than one…" continued the American lady. Fred seemed to visibly shrink again.

"M-m-more than one?" he stammered.

"Yes, the Lord Mayor managed four!"

"Four?" Fred gazed blankly around his shop, as if searching for an escape route. He saw us watching and the master butcher's agony was plain to see, written large across his face. You might ask if Woody and I were enjoying this? Yes, indeed we were… But we were soon to be deflated.

"I have to tell you, Fred, all of my family, friends and dignitaries at the barbecue thoroughly enjoyed those delicious hamburgers, they were voted the best they'd ever tasted. Thank you, Fred, you are a star! I'll be recommending your butcher's shop to everyone!"

After the American lady left the shop with a pork leg joint for her Sunday roast, Fred burst into song and danced a little jig around the shop.

'The speed achievable by such a portly chap astonished us!

"Great story Phil, have a pint on the house," beamed Bill the landlord. "Sorry about the missus giving you an earful earlier about the 'Soup in the Basket' joke. I for one thought it was hilarious! Kaz though, just couldn't see through it!"

"Cheers Bill, that's very kind of you. Make it a 'Yore Inn' please."

"We 'ad a butcher where we lived in Putney who was a bit like yours, Phil, slightly crooked. But his meat was the bee's knees," said Cockney taxi driver Chips.

"Bee's knees might be too sweet for me!" Bill the landlord observed.

# Antique Strobe Show

My good friend Rolland Charleston was a skilled craftsman. He used to, in his own words,‘ manufacture ’ antiques; or to be more precise, parts of antiques. In fact, he was an antiques restorer of such high quality that even the most learned trade experts have had great difficulty spotting Rolland's masterly repairs. Widely regarded as the best in his field of work, one of the methods he used is called ‘distressing’. I have seen him at work and yes I can easily see why the expression was coined.

The repaired item of furniture would be secured onto a bench. Then the newly fitted, usually lighter coloured replica part would be soundly whipped, with a bicycle chain dipped in old black engine oil. After a few hours of this treatment, eventually a random patination reminiscent of extreme age was produced, hopefully camouflaging the repair enough for it to blend in seamlessly with the rest of the antique.

Rolland often worked at home, in his cellar workshop. He and his wife Sally lived in a seventeenth century house, overlooking Warwick Racecourse.

A very kind gentleman of superb character and an upstanding, honest pillar of the community, Rolland would have been the first to admit that he had a very distinctive appearance. How can I put it? All right, he could easily have been cast as Rasputin the Mad Monk in a Hammer Horror film. He would not have needed excessive makeup. Piercing, askance dark eyes, a mop of unruly, jet-black hair, some missing digits and an unkempt beard complete the picture.

Rolland and his comfortably proportioned wife Sally were regular drinkers at The Miller's Arms and you could spot the pair easily as he always wore black and his wife generally wore white.

It was around eight o'clock when I entered 'The Milly' that Thursday night. I knew immediately there was something amiss between Rolland and Sally. The usually happy couple seemed a tad morose. As I joined them at a table near the bar, I had the distinct impression that you could have cut the atmosphere with a knife.

"What's up with you two?" I asked. "You look as if you've lost a tenner and found a penny! Cheer up, it may never happen!" I tried in vain to bring a smile to their glum faces.

Rolland rolled his eyes in mock agony. "It has already happened, mate!" He somehow managed to say this through clenched teeth. Quite a feat and perhaps he would make a good ventriloquist, I mused.

"It's all his fault," Sally pointed derisively at her husband.

"But I was only doing my bloody job!" he protested.

I was intrigued. "Tell me more," I pleaded, "it can't be that bad, surely?"

Rolland looked at the ceiling, got up and strolled

over to the bar to get drinks. “Your usual, Phil?” I nodded but was sure that it had been my round; perhaps Rolland just needed to get out of earshot of his beloved.

“What’s going on, Sally?” I asked again. “Something big, I guess?”

“Okay, I’ll tell you. it’s quite a tale of woe though, I’ll warn you!” She then began her illuminating story.

“You said, ‘It can’t be that bad,’ well it was that bad. It sounds unbelievable, but this is exactly what happened…”

“As you know, we are desperate to sell our house, The Old Stables; we’ve had it on the market now for over six months! We have a new house lined up, ready to make our move, but we have to sell ours first. Last night a young couple called round, by appointment, for a viewing. They seemed very impressed and looked very likely to buy it.”

As Sally answered the front door, she noticed the menacing dark clouds approaching. “I think we’re in for a storm,” she remarked to the young couple waiting on the steps.

“Thunder by the looks of it,” said the smartly dressed young man, who then made the introductions.

“I’m Mark and this is my wife Theresa, we’re here to view your house.” He propelled his pretty young partner up the steps.

“I’m Sally, pleased to meet you both, do come in.” Sally said, while holding the heavy door open and ushering them in.

Theresa was dressed in a light, summery blouse and

skirt. Sally hoped that she had a brolly in her large handbag; the first penny-sized drops of rain were starting to fall as she closed the door. Sally had the impression the pair liked the house from the start of their tour.

"Shall we start upstairs?" Sally suggested, leading the way.

"Oh, this is gorgeous," remarked the pretty girl. "I could definitely live here, Mark!" The stairway and landing were particularly well presented and featured original, hand-carved woodwork and the walls were finished in a warm burgundy. Mark nodded his agreement.

Weather predictions were confirmed a little later whilst viewing the master bedroom. The pair clung together for comfort in reaction to a far-off rumble of thunder, the young man's arm around his wife's shoulders. Sally guessed they would have been in their early twenties. A long time has passed since Roland had treated her in such a chivalrous fashion, she'd thought wistfully.

"It's okay, darling, we're safe here," the young man comforted his wife.

They absolutely loved the bedrooms. "Oh, look Mark, oak beams, diamond leaded dormer windows. I do like this," said Theresa.

"What's the view like, Sally?" Mark had to raise his voice to be heard above the rain, which was by now beating a cacophonous din on the window panes. They tried in vain to look out of the window but the black night was punctuated only by the occasional brilliance of God's flashlight. The thunder crashed closer.

"Well Mark, on a clear day," Sally emphasised, "you can see quite a lot of open countryside from this window, most of South Warwickshire in fact, oh, and Warwick Racecourse. My husband Rolland likes an occasional flutter on the horses. He often watches his selections 'going down 'through binoculars from this window!" She chuckled, but didn't think they'd got her feeble joke.

After viewing the spacious, well-equipped kitchen the pair were ushered into the parlour. With a huge log fire crackling away in the cosy inglenook fireplace, this room seemed so romantic and inviting. The host sat the pair down on the cosy old sofa and gave them hot drinks, biscuits and cakes. Sally was sure they were hooked on the place… everything was going so smoothly… surely nothing could go wrong?

"It says in the brochure that the house has a large, useful cellar," said Theresa excitedly, between delicate sips of Earl Grey tea and bites of Sally's homemade lemon drizzle cake.

"Can we see it please, Sally?" asked Mark eagerly, as he drained a mug of cocoa and picked up a digestive.

"Why yes, of course you can, and a very useful cellar it is too, as you will soon see. When we get down there, I'll introduce you to my husband Rolland. He's a furniture restorer and uses the cellar as a workshop." She glanced at her watch. "I think by now he'll be distressing."

A puzzled expression did flit across their faces, but Sally dismissed it, thought no more of it. Then the couple held hands. Bless them, she'd thought.

"This way, mind the steps, they're a bit steep!" Sally warned as she grabbed the torch and led the couple down the tightly-winding, steep, stone stairway.

The storm drew closer as the three descended into the bowels of the building. Sally kept the torch facing downwards to illuminate the steps, in the manner of a cinema usherette. She avoided pointing the beam upwards as that would have revealed a colony of spiders complete with an array of webs. In preparation for the visitors, she had cleaned scrupulously everywhere else, but somehow this part of the house had been overlooked.

As they neared the cellar door the sounds of Rolland at work grew gradually louder, echoing around the dank, sandstone passageway. First, they heard the rattling of chains clattering against the side of an oil drum, then a swishing sound and the thwack of slippery metal on wood. This was followed by a bout of heavy breathing, gasping and a little grunting.

The ancient studded oak door growled objectionably on its ancient rusty hinges as Sally pulled it open to reveal the master craftsman in full flow.

An upturned Victorian chair had been tethered firmly to a bench. Rolland was whipping one of the ornately carved wooden legs soundly with an oily old bike chain. His coal black eyes gleamed with enthusiasm, sweat was pouring copiously from his brow. His hair stuck out at odd angles, rather like a chimney sweep's brush that had seen better days. The rolled-up cigarette clenched between his lips forced them into a leering grin and provided a thin, ethereal cloud of blue-grey smoke.

Through a window high on the far cellar wall, a series of staccato lightning flashes created a strobe effect, illuminating the scene in electric blue slow motion. The usually dimly-lit cellar was transformed; Rolland appeared to be animated in his own unearthly discotheque light show. All this was accompanied with the by now very loud crashes of thunder.

"My, that storm is getting close!" observed Sally, pseudo-cheerfully, as she turned, preparing to educate her two young companions on the finer points of her husband's chosen profession.

She was wasting her breath.

She was talking to thin air.

She was staring at empty space.

"Our two young prospective house purchasers had fled the warm comfort of our beautiful house, dressed in light summer clothes, straight into the arms of a raging tempest!" Sally sobbed as she took a swig of lager and gave Rolland another disdainful look. "They never even said 'Goodbye'!"

"But I was only doing my bloody job," Rolland repeated.

A little later I noticed the pair making up, in each other's arms, in a corner near the bar. That is exactly what rows are for!

I'm glad to report that the house did sell, to a middle-aged couple, two months later.

Rolland in full flow.

# The Generous Sponsor

It was a cold winter's night and the The Story Teller's Chair in the bar of Warwick's fifteenth century Miller's Arms was the nearest to the fire. The rule is — If you sit in this chair, you must tell an amusing but true story. As soon as my rear had touched the seat, I was surrounded by an expectant audience.

I began: "This happened a few years ago, a friend called round to discuss a forthcoming outing:"

"You won't need to bring any sarnies, Phil," Norman advised, "there will be a free lunch before the rally starts… And free beer!" he added for good measure. It sounded good to me. "Be at my place about 7.30 a.m."

"I'll be there," I said, "see you Saturday!"

I really looked forward to this huge treat. A FREE coach trip and FREE entrance to The Duchies Rally in Charnwood Forest and FREE food and FREE drink! Add to that the excitement of seeing the top rally car drivers in action at a challenging location; I wouldn't have missed it for the world. Little did I realise though, it would be a day to remember for a totally different reason!

My best friend Norman had worked at the Purego car plant near Coventry for fifteen years and one of the perks of his job was that he and a companion were entitled to free trips to attend rallies organised by the Swiss car maker. He could invite a friend or spouse. Luckily for me, Mrs Norman 'would rather watch paint dry!'

As we left Norman's house in Coventry that Saturday morning, on our way to the coach pick up point, he presented me with his old red rally cap, emblazoned with the initials 'BGC', which I dutifully wore throughout the day. Just about everyone else, I noticed later, was wearing the brand new blue Purego Rally Team cap, complete with the company's unmistakeable large goat logo.

After a couple of hours on the coach, we alighted in the grounds of Spelbeck Abbey in Charnwood Forest, the beautiful location for that year's Duchies Rally Headquarters. The two of us strolled across the car park to peruse a large map showing the various rally stages proposed for that day.

After a few minutes spent perusing the map, a tall bespectacled man sporting a blue cap, with a baby strapped to his belly, sauntered over to join us. He kindly explained, in great detail, the various rally stages planned for that afternoon. "Of course, this all takes place after lunch, which will be served in that marquee over there, at one o'clock," he pointed to a large white tent on a lawn. "I look forward to seeing you in there later."

"Yes, see you later!" we chorused. The tall gentleman smiled as he wandered off with his gurgling cargo.

After the man with the baby had departed, Norman said, "Well I'm blowed. He is the manager of the Purego Rally Team. I'm amazed, in all the fifteen years I've been attending these rallies, he hasn't ever uttered a single word to me! And did you notice, he was speaking to you, Phil, not me?"

"I did think it odd, he didn't even acknowledge you Norm, and I'm just a guest for the day!" I remarked.

A little later we joined about two hundred other spectators in the huge marquee. We made our selection from the excellent buffet. I had a whitebait starter, sirloin steak with all the trimmings, followed by a portion of sherry trifle. We obtained a couple of free beers, found a table and settled down to a superb free lunch. A short while later Norman and I were presented with a large bottle of champagne which the waiter duly popped open for us. Good job, as we'd have struggled with the cork in the state we were in! We hadn't noticed anyone else having this exotic treat, but just got on with drinking it. We were just finishing our meal when a microphone crackled into life:

"Good afternoon ladies and gentlemen and welcome to The Purego Duchies Rally." It was the manager of the Rally Team, minus the baby. The crowd hushed, in anticipation.

He went on to describe the various events scheduled for that afternoon, and towards the end of his speech, he discussed funding. "We, at The Purego Rally Team, are hugely indebted and very grateful for the generous financial support from the Burnease Gas Company."

"And of course, none of this, yes, I'll repeat that,

NONE of this," he emphasised, "would be possible without the generous sponsorship from this very kind gentleman." He looked across to our table and pointed to me.

Yes, he WAS pointing straight at… ME! YES, ME!

There was a round of applause from all present except a startled Norman. Applause, for me? My head was whirring, in a fog of alcohol-induced confusion. I suddenly sat bolt upright, like a rabbit caught in the headlights.

The Rally Team Manager just stood there, quietly smiling at me through his glasses, clearly expecting some sort of response. I very nearly choked on my champagne. Every eye in the tent was on me, but my initial intent was to be out of that tent. Or should I remain? I was too tense! And slightly sloshed. Was this a dream? A nightmare? I tried in vain to wake up. No. It was real. This was happening.

I remember very clearly how time seemed to slow right down, as if I was viewing the event filmed on a high-speed camera, replayed at a very slow speed. Time stood still. Earth, open up now! I had ten pounds on me. Is he after that? I quickly dismissed the thought. I was trying to think on my feet. On my feet was a good idea. I stood up and smiled drunkenly back at the rally manager. He was, by now, at our table and pushing the microphone towards my reluctant mouth.

"Errr, no problem, I'm always glad to help the Purego Rally Team! Good luck to everyone this afternoon!" I smiled weakly and tried not to slur. It was short and sweet. But this seemed to satisfy all concerned. Everyone in the marquee stood up and I received yet another undeserved round of rapturous applause. I raised my champers glass in a sort of half-hearted toast. Then I gave what I hoped was an appreciative smile and wave, but it may well have been tinged with panic and horror.

Norman had noticed the only other red cap wearer in the sea of blue ones, across the other side of the marquee and pointed him out to me. The gentleman had a quizzical look on his face and was glancing from side to side. On his cap we could read 'B.G.C.'.

During that afternoon, during the rally I was dubbed Mister B.G.C. by fellow spectators.

A wheel whizzed through the air twenty feet above our heads as a four-wheel drive car came to an ignominious end in a ditch, facing whence it had come from.

"I did NOT sponsor that!" I declared.

I learned later from a friend who works for them, that I am a dead ringer of the gas company's financial director. I hope I did the handsome chap credit on the day!

"I'll bet you did, Phil! Can I sponsor a pint for you?" asked my pal Big Julie, from her usual corner of the bar.

"Ooooh yes, a pint of 'Yore Inn' for me please Julie."

Kaz pulled me a pint of the delicious, golden-yellow nectar, brewed here at The Miller's Arms, my favourite pub during the eighties and nineties.

If you're in the Warwick area I can recommend this pub. But don't sit in The Story Teller's Chair, the black plastic swivel one nearly in the fireplace, unless you have a good true tale to tell.

He pointed across to our table….

# Bitter and Twisted

Andy Grange did gamble. Definitely. Just remember that please, dear reader.

A half mile stroll down the road from The Miller's Arms led us to The Top Lock Inn. My old chum Ivan, the tall bald mechanic, was a semi-regular at this pub and I'd agreed to accompany him one balmy summer night, on a 'pub crawl'. A waterside beer garden was one of the pub's many attractions. But there were also pitfalls here…

'ANDREW GRANGE, licensed purveyor of wines, ales, spirits and tobacco, to be consumed on or off the premises.' declared the licensee's sign above the door. The canal-side, purpose-built, red-brick ale house was established originally for the 'Navvies' who constructed the Grand Union Canal as it passed though Warwick at the start of the nineteenth century.

Ivan was first in, so he ordered. "Two pints of best bitter please, Andy." The stockily built middle-aged landlord with long fair hair pulled two foaming pints of Ainsley's Best Bitter. A lighter drink than our usual 'Yore Inn' ale, but tasty nonetheless.

"That'll be three pounds sixty please, Ivan." Andy held his hand out and Ivan paid with a twenty-pound note. We had a slurp while Andy sorted the change. He handed some coins and a fiver over to Ivan.

"What's this?" asked the tall mechanic. "I gave you a twenty!" he spluttered, inadvertently ejecting some of the precious liquid in the landlord's direction.

"Yes, it was definitely a twenty-pound note." I backed up my pal.

"How much change have I given you?" asked Andy emotionlessly, in his soft Scottish brogue.

"Six pounds forty pence!" said Ivan, holding out his large, dinner-plate-size right hand, palm up, with all of the 'change' on display.

With a roll of his eyes Andy went back to the till and took out a tenner which he handed to Ivan without muttering a word of apology. Strange, I thought, the Scot seemed to look angry.

As soon as Andy went down to the cellar and out of earshot, we were joined by a short Jamaican chap, sporting a pork pie hat. "It ain't nuthin' special 'bout you, my man," he declared, looking Ivan squarely in the eye. "He tries to short change everyone. He was jus' annoyed that you rumbled him!" He gave a little giggle. "You gotta watch Andy. Andy Grange? Watch your change!" Other barflies chuckled and nodded in agreement.

"You're right Jimmy, he'd fiddle his own mother if he had a chance!" remarked a large, ginger-haired man with a well-developed beer paunch. "Win's okay though, she wouldn't dream of doing you. Salt of the Earth! Lovely girl!"

When I bought my round, I managed to find the

exact £3.60 in coinage in my pocket. I needn't have worried though, as Andy's delightful 'other half', Win served me. An attractive thirty-something brunette with model looks, she took my money with a cheery smile.

Later we returned to 'The Milly', in time for our last drink of that night. Landlord Bill was pleased to see us back, but we were still ejected from the pub at ten past eleven, as was the custom. Not a bad custom if you planned to be working the next day.

Although we were always concerned about 'Dodgy Andy' and his 'antics', the Top Lock Inn did have other attractions. The pub's glamorous landlady, Win, habitually wore rather daring, low-cut dresses and certain 'assets' were on display for 'Quantity Surveyors' at the bar. This happened to be a Win — win situation for The Top Lock. The pub held Ainsley Brewery's bottled brown ale annual sales record, mainly due to Win. She would have to bend forward to reach these bottles stored low down behind the counter. How her dress contents defied gravity is one of the wonders of the universe. Men gasped. Women tutted. Few bothered to order brown ale from ugly old Andy.

Another incentive was that the pub also operated a sort of after-hours service, for selected clients. So long as you were in the bar a good twenty minutes before closing time, you'd be invited to stay for a 'late one'. At closing time, Andy would announce, "Time, ladies and gentlemen, please!" to all and sundry as he rang a huge bell, followed ten minutes later by what he thought was an amusing rhyme: "Thank you for your glasses, now let's have your asses, out of the door!"

But if you were 'selected', he would give you a huge theatrical wink. This was the signal. We would sit tight and nurse the last few precious drops of ale in our glasses until the other, less desirable, wiser, or even mathematically superior, customers had left. We were then rewarded by the phrase "Would you like another drink chaps?" from Andy, pointedly looking at his watch as if to emphasise that this was indeed a 'treat' for which we should be very grateful. Of course, he would then proceed to 'short change 'customers in his usual fashion. No change there then.

The Top Lock Inn got well known to all Warwick ale aficionados, for its for 'lock ins'. When the licensed hours ended at eleven o'clock, or ten thirty on Sundays, Andy Grange also did something quite remarkable. Quite unusual. And he was quite open about it, all regulars knew and he'd happily tell anyone who asked. It was no secret…

As soon as the curtains were drawn at closing time, Andy cashed up the brewery's till and removed it. He then installed his own till. At the same time, he swapped the main Ainsley's Bitter Ale pump pipe line, connecting it instead to draw from his own barrel of ale. This was ale he'd bought from Mitch's Wine Merchant's in Leamington. Top Lock customers' perception was that Andy was not doing anything wrong.

The clientele largely didn't notice any difference as the spurious bitter tasted fine; at that time of night anyway. Andy stayed open as long as there was money to be had. As long as you had money in your pocket and were thirsty, you'd be welcome to continue drinking. On one occasion, we were nearly run over by a milk float on the way home! So in order to not miss out, my pal Ivan and I also became 'regulars' at this watering hole. We'd often start a 'liquid research' session at the 'Milly' and end up later at The Top Lock Inn lock in. This continued for many years. Don't ask how many. Many.

It was a few years later that Jimmy the Jamaican converted from 'The Top Lock Inn' and started to spend the well-earned cash from his antique emporium at 'The Milly' instead. We were not surprised. One cold, October Wednesday night, Jimmy, a seventy-year-old who somehow looked only fifty at the most, waddled over to The Story Teller's Chair and parked his bottom. A crowd soon assembled and hushed in anticipation. Jimmy set his pork pie hat at a jaunty angle and after taking a sip of 'Yore Inn', began his tale of woe…

"Now you all know I used to drink at The Top Lock, just down the road. Well, Andy the landlord there is a mighty twisted fellow and no mistaking!" Jimmy's Jamaican accent sounded a bit like Welsh, I'd thought.

Me and Ivan nodded in agreement. We knew all right. We'd adopted the habit of paying Andy using only five-pound notes, in an attempt at damage limitation. We'd not been using the 'Lock Inn' recently though.

"Not content with just short-changing folk to make some extra holiday spending money, he went one better, or so he thought. He started selling his own, non-brewery, late drinks to some folks."

"The police were fully aware of 'The Lock Inn lock ins' and because there was never any trouble, they chose to 'turned a blind eye' and 'let sleepin' dogs lie'. Also, it was well known that Andy's brother was the editor of The Warwick Morning Express. Now, as it happens, it might 'ave been better for Andy if the 'Feds' had put a stop to his little games there and then. Oh yes."

"The Top Lock Inn provided an excellent 'after hours' service for a good four years or so. Andy's wife Win used to go to bed soon after closing, leaving him to do his 'mischief' on his own. Favoured clients would be regularly and gently 'milked' of their cash. It was, to all intents and purposes, a perfect set up. Ainsley's Brewery got their daytime, 'in hours' takings, so no foul play was suspected. Andy made a huge fortune floggin' his own ale after hours. All was going so well. Then the Granges went and bought a house in Mill Way."

The audience gasped at this. Mill Way was the address of the rich and famous. Near the River Avon and opposite Warwick Castle. If you lived here, you'd made it. Big time.

Jimmy went on…

"Yep, the boy done good, you might say. For his detached, villa-style, six-bedroom house on Mill Way, Andy paid £180,000. Cash. Yep. I did say, Cash!"

Jimmy looked at his audience and saw what he wanted to see, surprise and awe.

"Yep, in cash, all in tens and twenties. Andy paid cash. Thinkin' this was best for him. No mortgage. No hassle gettin' a mortgage. No added interest. All this house was his. All paid for. All done and dusted. All sorted. All bad though. My missus, Lucy, uses the same hairdressers as Win, so she got this news 'from the horse's mouth'!"

"About three months after Andy and Win moved into their Mill Way mansion, one sunny September morning the doorbell rang. One o' them fancy tunes, y'know, 'Ding dong, ding dong…' like big, old, church bells, but playin' one o' them ice cream van chimes…"

Two sombre looking men in grey suits stood in Andy's porch. "Mr Andrew Grange?" asked the taller of the two, a balding, bespectacled man with a 'pelmet' of grey hair. Thick lenses gave him an owlish look.

"Yes, that's me. Good morning, gentlemen, how can I help you?" asked Andy.

"We are from the Inland Revenue, Mr Grange. May we come in?" asked the shorter of the two, sporting a full head of mousey hair and carrying a clipboard. He showed an I.D. card.

"Yes, do come in," invited Andy. "What is this about?"

"Nice house, Mr Grange. Do you gamble?" This was a simple question from the tall taxman.

"Oh no, I've never gambled in my life," lied Andy. It was well known to his customers that he'd often won on his own sweepstakes at The Top Lock Inn.

"Are you sure you've never gambled?" asked the shorter man, writing furiously on his clipboard. "Never, ever?"

"No, I do not gamble and never have," Andy replied. Wrong answer. The Scot was getting a tad agitated. "Now can you kindly explain what all this is about?"

"As I said, we're from the Inland Revenue and we are very interested to know how you financed this lovely large house, Mr Grange," the short man explained.

"Oh, is that all? Well, that's simple. I bought it for one hundred and eighty thousand pounds, in cash, using my savings. Now would you two gents like a coffee before you go?" Andy thought he'd salved the two curious taxmen's curiosity.

"That's very kind of you, yes please," said the taller official, peering owl-like at Andy through his thick glasses. The shorter taxman nodded that he'd also like a coffee.

Andy proudly led the two men into his huge kitchen. Patio doors opened from this room onto decking and a vast striped lawn lay beyond. He prepared coffee for three. Maybe he would have added something sinister to two of the mugs if he'd known in advance what was to come…

"Thank you," said the pair of tax inspectors in unison, accepting the mugs of delicious Camp Coffee and sitting on stools at the huge kitchen table. Andy offered them digestive biscuits. They took two each and the tall official proceeded to 'dunk' his, seemingly to the annoyance of his colleague. This amused Andy.

"What a marvellous view, is that the River Avon?" asked the taller official. He'd noticed a swan apparently sailing effortlessly across Andy's lawn.

"Why yes, and from the verandah upstairs, we can see Warwick Castle!" Andy smiled. All in the world seemed so rosy at that moment. Nice house, all his. His gorgeous wife Win had gone shopping in Leamington Spa in his brand-new Jaguar. They'd both recently retired from the pub trade. Too many late nights! Sitting in his huge kitchen, with the two tax inspectors, enjoying a coffee, looking across his immaculate striped lawn down to the river. Bragging, even, about his lovely new house. Nothing on earth could spoil Andy's feeling of sheer bliss right now. Nothing. Surely?

"You say you paid for this house with money you had saved?" asked the shorter man.

"Exactly. So there's no mortgage to worry about, it's all paid for!" Andy smiled. He thought that was the end of it. "Okay, gentlemen," Andy looked at his watch, "I'm sorry, but I'll have to ask you chaps to leave now. I have an appointment at my dentist in half an hour," he lied.

"We have just one problem with what you have told us, Mr Grange," remarked the taller man, draining his mug and rising from the table, "according to your tax record, you have never, in your whole life, earned anywhere near enough to pay for this house!"

"And you have already confirmed to us, twice this morning, that you have never gambled. Never ever. So you couldn't have won the money to pay for this house. Mr Grange, there are many questions that we at Inland Revenue will have to ask," warned the short official. "We will be back. You will be hearing from us very soon."

As the two tax inspectors left, they left Andy in a worried state. Win suspected something was amiss when she returned from shopping later that day. When she showed her husband the new bright yellow dress she'd bought at Rackham's, he seemed disinterested, distracted, maybe even distraught?

"Well," continued Jimmy, "a month or so after the two taxmen visited Andy, Lucy, my missus, heard some more news:"

"Hey, Jimmy, have you heard the latest about the Granges?" Lucy asked excitedly, while unloading some shopping at my antiques shop in the High Street.

"Ain't seen them for months," I replied. "Why, what's happened?"

"Well, I heard this from my hairdresser: You remember that they bought that fancy big house down Mill Way, after leaving the pub?"

"Yeah, I remember. Paid cash didn't they, and then they had an unwelcome visit from the tax people?"

"That's right. Beth, my stylist, says Win told her that Andy had a major tax fraud investigation. The brewery got involved and sued him too. The Granges ended up having to sell their house to pay the brewery damages and the tax demand. Now they have nothing. Even their new car had to go." Lucy went on, "Beth said Win was in tears when she told her."

"Wow, that's 'just desserts' for Andy, but poor Win. She didn't deserve to have that happen. Lovely girl," observed Chips, our part-time, part-retired Cockney taxi driver.

As soon as Jimmy vacated the Story Teller's Chair, Henry sat down on the uncomfortably still warm seat. The audience re-assembled to hear what our Miller's

Arms regular taxman and unpaid tax advisor had to say. He began:

"The lesson here is clear. If asked by the taxman, you always admit to gambling. You can then claim that you either won, or lost a certain amount, according to your circumstances. Keep some betting slips lying around though! And generally, paying huge amounts of cash will alert the authorities to possible money laundering activities." Many nodded. This was sound advice from Henry.

"Andy was a fiddling bastard by all accounts though! But you've got the end of your story slightly wrong, Jimmy!" declared the slim, sandy-haired civil servant.

"What d'you mean, Aitch?" Jimmy was astounded. "I honestly thought I'd got it right." The audience soon re-assembled to hear what the taxman had to say.

"Actually, the Granges did not sell their house, Jimmy. Oh no, far from it. The Inland Revenue seized it and sold it at auction to pay the penalties for the four years fraudulently evaded tax. A portion of the damages awarded to the brewery was also paid from the sale of the Grange's criminal assets," declared Henry. "I should know. Don't forget, I work for the local tax collection office. And there's some more facts you folks might find interesting…"

The assembled audience hushed and waited with bated and beer laden breath.

"The Grange's Mill Way mansion was snapped up at the auction for the bargain hammer price of only £130,000! That's £50,000 less than they'd paid for it!"

All present gasped in amazement. But there was still

more to come. Henry drained his glass of amber Yore Inn Ale before continuing:

"Another thing, the winning bidder was a tall, balding chap called Miles Potter. He's a colleague of mine at the tax office. He has a 'pelmet' of grey hair and wears thick glasses."

"Well, that's just taking the biscuit!" Once again Chips had the last word.

Update: Win left Andy and moved to Stratford-upon-Avon where she opened and successfully ran a souvenir shop. Andy moved back to his native Scotland.

The Warwick Morning Express declined to report on the case. Brotherly love?

What a marvellous view. Is that the river Avon?

# High Notes

My young friend Norman has the distinction of being the highest paid live pub musician ever… yet he is no Elton John, far from it!

One summer Friday night, Norman, a tall, handsome twenty-five-year-old car factory worker from Coventry, dropped by for a jar at The Miller's Arms. When I explained about the tradition of telling true stories whilst sitting on our hallowed 'throne', he immediately sat on it and started to tell the regulars this very amusing one about himself:

I like to think that I have a reasonable singing voice and that I am not too bad at 'tinkling the ivories'. I have often been asked to perform at family gatherings and have always hankered after the chance to prove my talents in front of a wider audience. So when the opportunity arose, I grasped it with both hands…

Having recently acquired a new Yamaha keyboard, I was feeling suitably buoyant when I gave a short audition at a local pub. I managed to convince George, the middle-aged balding landlord of The Rampant Bull in Fillongley, that I could provide 'live music' at his pub. George said that he felt there was a need to get ‘more feet through the door’ on certain sessions. So a gig was arranged for a Saturday night, as this was usually a quiet one for the pub.

The price agreed was eighty pounds for the night. How many encores, I wondered, would I be pestered into playing? Would anyone ask for my autograph? I was overjoyed at the prospect of my very first professional engagement.

A few days later I swelled with pride when I saw the half page advert George had placed in the local paper:

**Singer / Songwriter Norman Dee debuts live at The Rampant Bull,**
**Fillongley.**
**Saturday 19th August, 8 p.m.**

This was complemented with some fantastic artwork involving a keyboard, crotchets, quavers and treble clefs on a lurid striped background. The Coventry Evening Telegraph graphics department had gone into overdrive.

“That’s me!” I exclaimed excitedly, on seeing a similar ad in the village post office window a few days later. The only recipient of this information, a small freckle-faced boy on a cycle, cast me a nervous glance and pedalled off at a furious rate.

I decided to design, print and distribute some of my own home-made posters for the event myself. Soon every telegraph post or spare bit of wall in Fillongley was festooned with my brightly coloured ads. I should have apologised to anyone searching for the village telephone box during those weeks as they would, I’m afraid, have searched in vain. It was transformed from its usual bright red to the lurid blue and yellow I had chosen for my flyers.

One regret is that I should have used a more waterproof poster paint, for when it rained heavily on the Friday before the big day, my efforts were transformed into a dreadful, mossy green colour. It looked as though the whole village was under attack from some strange, alien fungus.

That Saturday evening soon came round. I arrived at The Rampant Bull all bright and bushy-tailed at 7.30 p.m., well in time for the scheduled 8 p.m. start. I was wearing very large dark sunglasses and had turned up my shirt collar, which I felt was de rigueur for the occasion. I certainly attracted some warm smiles as I entered the bar, which I was pleased to see was already heaving with customers eagerly awaiting the treat. One chap with a camera snapped me a couple of times and my ego swelled in the glare of the flashlight.

When he had a chance, George gave me a huge smile and a double 'thumbs up' from behind the bar. He was very busy indeed. I noticed that there were two extra barmaids on duty. Usually, on a Saturday night, George and his wife Vera managed by themselves. This was all boding very well.

I had to squeeze gingerly past throngs of drinkers as I ferried in my keyboard and amplifiers and arranged them in a corner near the bar. I did my best to keep the wires tidy, but somehow they still ended up looking like an absurd tangle of black spaghetti. Eight o'clock arrived, the crowd waited with bated and beer-laden breath.

At eight o'clock precisely I cleared my throat and proudly announced, "Good evening, ladies and gentlemen… and George." This raised a mild titter and my audience, momentarily silenced, hung attentively on my every word.

"My name is Norman Dee and I'm here to entertain you tonight with some of my own songs. This first one, a brand-new composition, is called 'Yellow Dog Blues', a ballad about a journey across America's Deep South in the company of a hound dawg." I placed the mike in its holder then struck the keyboard and burst bravely into song.

"Ahh bin travlin' overland, over water, by the sand, wi' mahh hound dawg at my hand…" I began singing what I thought was one of my best offerings. 'This'll get them going,' I'd thought…

The background cacophony of chatter and laughter punctuated with the clinking of glasses gradually ceased. Mouths gaped open halfway through slurping drinks, in suspended animation.

Awestruck, all eyes turned towards the source of the sounds. Sounds that they were hearing for the very first time in their lives. Sounds that they would never forget. Sounds that would be the subject of many conversations. Sounds that children would be regaled about in future generations, "Son, I was THERE, in The Rampant Bull that very same Saturday night when it all began for Norman Dee. Yes, THE Norman Dee!"… I'd imagined.

As I played and sang, I looked again at the eyes of

the audience, trying to gauge their mood. Surely that was rapture? admiration? grudging approval? Or could I detect jealousy? Whatever it was, my performance was certainly having an effect.

My talents as a singer and songwriter soon became obvious to all present. I'd had an immediate effect on takings... and customer numbers. You can judge the quality of my performance by the crowd's reaction.

At first, the rate of beer consumption actually soared, momentarily, as customers gulped down drinks in record time. But all too soon, the reason for emptying their glasses in a hurry became obvious; it was not because of thirst, or anxiety over whether or not there would be enough beer left in the barrel. Oh no.

With horror, I noticed that my very first public audience, fans even, or more importantly The Rampant Bull's precious customers, were leaving the premises in droves! This was 'Feet through the door' all right, but the wrong way!

To add to that, potential fans and customers approaching The Rampant Bull's doors were doing a u-turn, joining the mass exodus. The village's other pub, The White Swan, just down the road, might benefit, I'd thought.

By the time I had started my second number, 'Stepping Out', there were only three stalwart cider drinkers and an appreciative cat left in the pub with me and George.

George swiftly opened the till, whipped out eighty pounds in crisp twenties, sprinted over and presented this to me with a special request. In fact, the only request of the evening, "Please, Norman, stop playing! We're losing customers!" He pleaded, pressing the notes into my hand.

In his haste to return to the bar, George tripped over one of my stray wires, launching him into a spectacular headfirst dive. He landed sitting unceremoniously on a beer-soaked patch of carpet. The pub cat gave him a curious look.

I took the money and the hint and ceased playing. I looked at my watch. It was only four minutes past eight. George had already sent his extra two bar staff home early and Vera went upstairs to watch The Generation Game on TV.

Before packing and loading my gear, I sauntered over to join the three Stalwart Cider drinkers. "Hi, I'm Norman," I introduced myself, as it turned out unnecessarily.

"We know who you are! I'm Arthur and this is my mate Fred and his missus, Mable," said the shorter man. I detected that there must be a mouth somewhere in amongst Arthur's damp, yellow-grey, unkempt beard behind the pint glass. I winked when a frothy droplet of moisture, possibly having an ABV of 6% landed near my left eye.

Mable misread this and winked back at me. "That wasn't too bad a performance Norm, I reckon you should've 'ad a standin' ovulation!" she consoled, with genuine concern written all over her lived-in face, bless her.

"Your first gig, Norman?" asked Fred, the tallest of the trio, in a knowing way. I noticed that the veins combined with a few spots on his yellow face gave him the look of a well-used AA road map of The Midlands. I was sure I could recognise Redditch with its many roundabouts.

"There'll be more, an' you'll be bloody famous!" spluttered Arthur. The Landlord looked over and cut him a withering glance.

But I was cheered by the threesome's kindly attitude and I felt flush with my easily-gained wealth. I decided to buy a round. "Four pints of Stalwart, please, George." The Landlord was silent, I'd hoped he wasn't bitter. "And have one yourself!" I added generously. George managed a grudging grunt.

The four pints of Stalwart Cider arrived on the bar and I duly paid for five. I guess George pocketed the dosh in lieu of his, as I didn't see him drinking.

"Four minutes work for eighty pounds," I reflected to my three newly-found, rheumy-eyed companions, or fans even, since the very moment I had supplied their drinks.

Then after a swift mental calculation it suddenly dawned on me. A smile slowly spread across my face. "Four minutes work for eighty pounds; that's twelve hundred pounds an hour! This must surely be a record rate for a live pub singer?"

My fans and I raised our glasses and gave a big cheer. George shook his head in disbelief.

The Miller's audience was suitably impressed.

"I bet even Elton John would struggle to top that rate," observed Chips the Cockney taxi driver, wryly.

"Fancy a cider, Norman?"

"We've got Thrasher's or Bullfinch's. We don't do 'Stalwart," said Bill the landlord.

"Thrasher's will do fine," answered Norman. "Thanks, Chips."

This was 'Feet through the door' alright!"

# The Petrol Fairy

An audience soon congregated in The Miller's Arms bar as a middle-aged gent with a distinct sandy coloured comb-over hairdo occupied the Story Teller's Chair one Thursday night. We'd seen this chap occasionally in the bar with Ivan, our very own motoring expert and mechanic. Casually dressed in a light grey checked sports jacket and blue strides, he'd be around fifty years old, I guess. A fair-sized audience soon gathered and we were about to be awestruck by the sheer audacity of his true story:

"Hello, I'm Don," he began, "I buy and sell second-hand cars now and then, to support my income as a mechanic. I suppose some people would describe me as 'a bit of a shark'! All I can say to them is that I've got mouths to feed, so needs must. This story is about a car I bought and sold in the late seventies. It presented me with a few headaches, but I overcame these using some rather unusual methods, to say the least!"...

"Yes, this car may look almost new, but it has got a couple of problems, Don," explained my mate Jamie, a local second-hand car dealer. I often bought trade-ins from him, and this old Rover 3.5 Automatic on a K-plate had been taken as a deposit against a Transit van.

It looked a minter in his yard, compared to some of the 'sheds' he had on display. It was finished in 'Moonraker Blue' metallic, with a black vinyl roof and no sign of the usual 'bodge' around the rear wheel arches. So it really was a rarity, and in the right colour.

"What's up with it?" I asked, surveying the smart-looking upmarket saloon. "Looks okay to me!"

"It's only doing about ten miles to the gallon and the clock reads 190,000 miles," replied Jamie, honestly and apologetically while stroking his long ginger beard. I'd often worried about how on earth he managed to keep this foot-long hairy appendage from being entangled in fan belts, when working on running engines.

I could fully understand why Jamie hadn't bothered to adjust the mileage on this Rover himself. Jamie had 'done time' for 'clocking'; the offence of falsifying — or 'correcting', as we traders prefer to call it — recorded vehicle mileages, a couple of years ago.

"Oh dear," I said, "well, I can probably sort out little snags like that. How much do you want for it?'

"It owes me four and a half."

I checked in my Glass's Guide. "Bottom book's three fifty. There's a bit of work to do…"

We haggled for a minute or two, and a little later I drove sedately home, £400 lighter, in a bargain banger that would soon be advertised in the local Morning Express as a 'Low Mileage Prestige Luxury Saloon', for the best part of fifteen hundred quid. The fuel gauge though, was a bit worrying; it moved so fast I mistook it for the speedometer!

That weekend I set to work on the Rover. A little cosmetic adjustment was called for on the recorded mileage, but I was in for a shock. As I disconnected the cable from the bulkhead ready to attach my drill, a little hand-written note dropped out. On it was scrawled: 'OH NO, NOT AGAIN!'

My high-speed drill soon reversed the high mileage, down to a much more acceptable 73,000 recorded miles. The mileage now matched the car's youthful looks. Didn't want to confuse customers, did I?

Those were 'The Good Old Days'. You can't adjust recorded mileages so easily these days. Modern cars are too complicated, all digital computer mumbo-jumbo. I'd often wondered, what was the real mileage on that Rover?

The next area for improvement was under the bonnet. The engine bay looked very grimy, only to be expected on a car that's probably been to the moon and back! But I soon fixed that with a nifty little trick I'd learned from some car trade friends.

First, I steam-cleaned the whole engine bay, and then, after I'd dried it thoroughly, I sprayed everything with clear lacquer. I kid you not, the effect of this treatment was ASTOUNDING. The engine and all ancillary equipment looked even better than it would have done when it was brand new! The main thing to remember while doing this is that you must dry the high-tension leads and distributor cap thoroughly inside and out or the engine might not start. I should probably add a warning here: 'DON'T TRY THIS AT HOME!'.

As far as the fuel consumption was concerned, I

decided to cross that bridge when I came to it. Anyway, football was on telly and I had an ad to write…

**1971 ROVER 3500 V8 AUTOMATIC**
**PRESTIGE LUXURY SALOON**
**Pristine condition. Low mileage**
**Finished in Moonraker Blue Metallic**
**first to see will buy. £1,495**
**WARWICK 988000**

A week or so later, Barry, a hefty security guard, who happened to live just around the corner from me, responded to my display advert in The Morning Express.

"These Rovers are a bit thirsty, aren't they?" Barry asked, as he examined the sinuous clean blue bodywork. He unnervingly reminded me of a police officer in his smart black uniform.

"Not at all," I replied. "This one does about twenty-five miles to the gallon if you take it easy." Of course I was lying through my teeth!

Barry sat in the driver's seat and put one hand on the steering wheel. He stroked his crew cut with the other as he viewed the freshly polished dashboard. The array of instruments was impressive, reminiscent of an aircraft's cockpit.

I gave him the keys. "Start it up Barry, take her for a test drive," I invited quickly. I'd seen him looking towards the mileage.

Barry turned the ignition key and the huge V8 Buick engine roared reassuringly into life. After revving it a few times, he selected 'D' and drove off towards the Warwick by-pass.

Nearly half an hour had passed before the Rover's return. "It drives okay, what's it like under the bonnet, Don?" he asked, turning the engine off and getting out.

I then delivered my *piece de resistance*: "I dunno, swapped it for a Transit van the other day, ain't had a look yet!" This was another slight porky. I lifted the bonnet. That was all I had to do. As I did so, I allowed my jaw to drop theatrically as I feigned absolute surprise and astonishment. "Bloody hell, Barry, the last owner certainly looked after this car! If I'd known it was this good I'd've asked for more money!" The way these last lines were delivered would have qualified as an Oscar-winning performance, I can assure you!

As I held the bonnet aloft, Barry's eyes widened in sheer awe at the sight of the engine bay glistening in the late afternoon's low sunlight. Nuts and bolts shone out like the Crown Jewels against the gleaming black serpent-like hosepipes. It was not just an engine bay; it was more like Aladdin's Cave!

"Wow," exclaimed Barry, almost breathlessly, eyes agog, reaching for his wallet. "Yeah, I'll buy it."

Barry swallowed the bait, hook line and sinker. He handed over my asking price of fourteen ninety-five in cash without any haggling whatsoever and drove off in the Rover with such a huge smug grin on his face, he reminded me of that Muppet, Dr Teeth.

Unfortunately, the next time I saw Barry this expression had, err, changed somewhat…

I bumped into him a week later whilst walking my

dog near his house. Okay, I had tried unsuccessfully to dodge him by crossing the road and looking intently in the other direction, but I wasn't quick enough and he ran across the road and grabbed my arm. Alan my Rottweiler luckily behaved himself.

"Hey, Don, you swine, that car you sold me," the well-built man spluttered angrily, "it's bloody awful on petrol; I can only get about ten miles to the gallon out of it," he complained grumpily. "You told me it would do twenty-five miles to the gallon!" It was all he could do to keep his big hands off me.

"It probably only needs tuning, Barry," I tried to console him. "Tell you what, bring it round to Brackley's Garage in Leamington. That's where I work. I'll tune it for you free of charge using the company's latest diagnostics machine," I offered generously.

"Right, I'll bring it in tomorrow morning on my way to work. Luckily, I'm on days for the next few weeks," he grunted menacingly.

As he uttered those words, the embryonic seed of an idea, possibly the solution to this slight problem, took root in my brain...

The car was duly delivered to Brackley's Garage the next morning. "You'd better make a bloody good job of tuning it Don, and if I don't get twenty-five miles to the gallon out of it, there'll be trouble, with a capital T," threatened the disgruntled security guard, as he threw me the keys.

My wife Muriel had warned me when she learned who'd bought the Rover, "I was at school with Barry, he had a reputation for being a bit of a 'bruiser'. Go careful with him, Don, I know we live near Warwick Hospital but I don't want to be visiting you in there!"

The Rover 3.5 executive saloon sat all day in Brackley's Garage's customers car park, without going anywhere near the new, four grand diagnostic machine. The eight-cylinder engine remained untuned and untouched by any mechanic. Barry's pride and joy did not move an inch from where he'd parked it. I did cut a spare key though, which I kept.

I tried to reassure the big security guard when he collected his car later that day. "It should be a lot better on petrol now that I've tuned it, Barry," I lied, while smiling at the big man. He did not return my smile.

"We'll see," grunted Barry as he drove off angrily, with tyres smoking and squealing. I winced at the thought of just how much precious petrol he was wasting, driving like a maniac.

Eight hours later I began the *coup de grace…*

At around 1 a.m. the next morning, I got up, donned my sheepskin jacket, slipped into some slippers, picked up a large bag, left the house and walked around the corner to where I found Barry's car parked as usual, in the road outside his house.

I returned home a little later feeling very pleased with myself. In just ten minutes, I had accomplished an elaborate deception involving the Rover 3500. Using my ingenious 'special treatment', I had managed to make the large saloon appear as economical as a Mini!

During the next week, each morning at around 1 a.m., I popped round the corner to Barry's car to do my 'good deed'.

Towards the end of the second week of this 'treatment', Barry stopped by one afternoon whilst I was doing some topiary on the privet hedge in my front garden. My nerves must have been on edge, as when Barry spoke, I accidentally snipped off a peacock's tail which I'd been nurturing for three years.

It was amazing though, to see what a few minutes remedial treatment in the middle of the night could do for a person's temperament. My previously disgruntled customer and neighbour was, it seemed, at a stroke, transformed from a blood-spitting, psychotic, rabid animal, into a sweet and saintly soul, full of the joys of life. Definitely a changed man. Restores your faith in human nature, it does.

"All right, Don?" asked the security guard in a friendly fashion.

"I'm fine thanks Barry, how's the Rover?" I'd hoped he hadn't noticed the slight quiver in my voice.

"Oh, it's great, thanks. By the way, about that tuning you did, I can't thank you enough, mate. It certainly did do the trick!" Barry was positively beaming with delight. "I'm amazed at just how economical my Rover 3500 is! My old Morris Minor used to guzzle twice as much petrol. I reckon I must be getting close on forty miles to the gallon. Unbelievable!"

It was nice to see such a happy, satisfied customer. It made all the efforts I'd been putting in each night seem so worthwhile.

I couldn't resist. "Yes, I thought it only needed tuning, glad to help Barry." I continued with my novice efforts with the hedge. What was supposed to be a peacock would now need to be modified into a goose.

"You've missed a bit!" the security guard joked, slapping his thigh, eyes full of merriment. "Thanks a lot Don, see you around," he said amiably, as he strolled off with the big happy smile reinstated on his face.

It is a great shame, but all good things must come, eventually, to an end. A Rover 3.500, with its huge V8 Buick engine, cannot possibly compete with a Morris Minor 1,000 for fuel economy, on the normal scale of things. Not in the real world. My little deception, nay, 'generous treat' as I like to think of it, had, alas, to finish. But I would do this gradually and gently... very gently.

The next morning, at around one o'clock, the alarm went off and I got up as usual. "You've been treating that Rover every night for two weeks," complained Muriel. "How much longer will you have to keep it up?" Muriel was a party to my little schemes. Indeed, over the years, she'd become accustomed to and even lent a hand with some of them.

"Oh, I'm starting to reduce it now darling, another few days or so, I suppose," I explained, as I pulled on a coat and set off on my regular nocturnal excursion.

If Barry had cared to look out of his front bedroom window, in the early hours during those weeks, he would have been astonished. He would have seen a man wearing a sheepskin coat, pyjamas and slippers lurking near his pride and joy carrying a huge carrier bag. He would have thought that the man was acting very suspiciously indeed.

He would have seen me looking furtively around before unlocking the fuel filler cap on his car with my copied key and placing a funnel into the aperture. He might have suspected that I was syphoning off his precious fuel. But, oh no, far from it, quite the opposite in fact.

Barry would have been amazed, gob-smacked even, to see me pour in, from a jerry can, at least half a gallon of premium petrol.

Not many car dealers would have gone to such great lengths. Just think, at a stroke I had ensured not just absolute customer satisfaction, but also, importantly, the non-escalation of local violent crime. Add to that the obvious psychological benefits; Barry, or 'Dr Teeth' as Muriel and me now refer to him, was blissfully happy. He was often seen out giving his wife and kids joy rides in his Rover 3.5 executive saloon.

I gradually reduced the amounts of fuel on the last few nights, to 'wean' my client off this luxury… gently, very gently.

"Have you bought a car from me? I am still trading!"

A roar of laughter erupted in The Miller's Arms.

"Crikey Don, you've certainly got a nerve!" remarked Bill the landlord, whilst pouring a pint of ale. "Great story though, have this Yore Inn on the house! By the way, I had to bar that Barry last year. He's a real troublemaker!"

"That's a great tip about cleaning the engine bay, Don," remarked our semi-retired Cockney taxi driver Chips. "I might try that on my old Vauxhall."

"I wouldn't bother, Chips, it's the inside of your taxi that needs steam cleaning!" observed Big Julie. "I should know, I'm your best customer!"

The Petrol Fairy at work.

# Post Heist

It only takes one evil-minded person in a position of power within an honourable organisation to create absolute chaos. The sheer audacity unveiled in this story beggars belief. Here we see how a fine, upstanding, hard-working family were metaphorically 'trampled underfoot' in a blind, callous stampede for wealth by one greedy, rogue, autocratic 'Regulator' working within a respected and trusted monopoly. I know, I do bang on about it, but if you read this, you'll see why…

Mike Cross and his wife Delia were occasional customers of The Miller's Arms. Sometimes they were accompanied by their tall, good-looking, police cadet son, Neal. My wife Jill and I played darts with them so we got to know them very well. We stuck by and supported the Cross family throughout the very turbulent and disturbing events that followed…

I remember clearly the night Mike revealed their plans. He'd recently retired from working for fifteen years as a sales representative in the motor trade.

"We sold our house on Emscote Road last week for the thirty-eight grand asking price," announced Mike proudly one Tuesday night, during a darts match at The Miller's Arms, in 1984. Six foot tall and with wavy, prematurely silver hair, Mike was always turned out well. That night, he was wearing a smart blue blazer, white shirt and chinos. Delia, only slightly shorter than her husband, was a straight-haired brunette with film star looks. Okay, she was so youthful looking she could be, and often was, assumed to be Mike's daughter! Tonight, she wore a smart cream two-piece outfit which complimented Mike's outfit perfectly.

"It'll be so good to not have to continually paint everything that bloody awful green!" Delia remarked. It was well known to all regulars that the Crosses had owned a house with a strict leasehold covenant. This compelled them to always redecorate the exterior only in the landowner's corporate drab green colour. "We've bought a post office in Solihull which was exactly the same price. And we've made sure we can paint it any colour we damn well like! What about purple, Mike?" she joked.

"No, I think we'll stick with post office red darling, we don't want to rock the boat, do we?" Mike threw three darts and got a cheer from his team when he scored one hundred and eighty. After winning his game, he turned to my wife Jill, with a suggestion: "There might be a job going for a part-time post office cashier, Jill, three days a week, if you're interested? And I can give you a lift there and back each day."

"Thanks for asking me Mike, it sounds good. I'll give it some thought overnight and let you know first thing tomorrow, if that's okay?" Jill would appreciate the extra dosh, I'd thought.

Jill sounded excited on the 'phone the next morning. "Yes, Mike, I'll take you up on the offer of that job!"

She was keen to get started.

After a couple of weeks working Wednesdays, Thursdays and Fridays, Jill said, “I love working for Mike, he’s a great boss! Oh, and there’s one thing I’ve learned. He told me that his shop cost twice the price of a similar-sized shop next door. The higher price was because Mike’s shop is a designated post office!”

Three years passed by very quickly and my wife happily worked part-time as a counter clerk throughout this time. Then, one Wednesday night, just before teatime, Jill arrived home and announced the shock news: “Guess what? Mike’s going to sell the Hillfield post office! He’s got it on the market and advertised the vacancy for a postmaster!”

I was shocked. The extra money had helped immensely, especially now our son Lee was about to start primary school.

“I suppose the new owner might not be able to keep you on and give you a lift each way?”

“That’s what I’m thinking, Phil. Just have to wait and see.”

Mike interviewed many prospective buyer-applicants, and they appeared to meet both criteria; the stringent post office rules and had the money to invest. In order to become both a postmaster and the owner of the shop seemed to require quite a lot of hoops to be jumped through. The area post office counter regulator rejected all of Mike’s hopeful applicants. Every one. Bar none.

Mike entered ‘The Milly’ one Monday night in

September, looking the worse for wear. I bought him a pint and pointed out my latest work of art, in an attempt to cheer him up. Above the bar was an old, black, oak beam on which I'd sign written in white paint: 'When I read about the evils of drink, I decided to give up reading!' Even Kaz, our dour landlady, had smiled at this effort. But not Mike. "How are things with you?" I asked.

Mike's reply revealed a huge problem. "You know that I've been trying for months to find a buyer for our shop, that's also acceptable to the post office, Phil?"

"Yes, Jill keeps me in the picture. They're pretty fussy at the post office, aren't they? Have you found anyone yet?" I asked.

"No. I've conducted six more interviews in the last week. All were rejected. But there's worse news. The Regulator, a lady by the name of Susan Topping, has decided our shop will no longer be a post office in one month's time. Whether we sell it or not. Her decision alone, and she won't change her mind. Bitch." Mike drew a deep breath. He was very agitated. I'd never seen him quite so upset before.

"This means we'll only get half of the price we paid for the shop. The thirty-eight grand investment will be reduced to nineteen grand only, because our shop will no longer be a post office. It'll sell only stationery and haberdashery. Not being a post office also means less customers, less customers means less income..." he tailed off.

"Can the shop sell other stuff though?" I asked. "Jewellery maybe?"

"Won't make any difference, Phil. The added value is in it being a post office."

"I'm sorry to hear that, Mike. A real shocker. What can you do?"

"We'll see." Mike winked at me as he finished his pint. He then sloped off without his usual cheery 'goodbye'. I had no idea at the time, but I would not see Mike again for many years.

When I told Jill later that night, she was in tears and rang Mike. With his agreement she decided to hand in her notice to relieve Mike's finances. He said that his wife Delia would 'step in' and cover Jill's counter duties, for the last couple of weeks. Very soon after that, we were to hear some astonishing news.

The Hillfield post office, at ten to nine on a Thursday morning, two weeks later, was like many others in the eighties. A long queue of about fifty people waited patiently in the drizzle, for the hallowed doors of Mike's shop to open. Their Giro cheques were due to be cashed in on that day, but only at this post office. This money was essential for benefit claimants. The money would, for most, be spent on food and other essentials. The queue waited. And lengthened. Nine o'clock came and went. The doors remained firmly shut.

"Wonder why they're so late opening?" Nobby, a bulky, greying, middle-aged, unemployed factory worker asked no one in particular. "They're usually open at exactly nine o'clock, on the dot!"

'Yeah, if they don't open soon, I'll be late for work," revealed a middle-aged, plump lady in a plastic mac. "Oh, I mean, for unpaid, voluntary work, of course," she corrected herself, looking around anxiously. Nobody had taken a blind bit of notice.

"Well, I've got kids to feed, so they'd better get a bloody move on!" Being first in the now very long and increasingly damp queue, Nobby tried the door at ten past nine. He tried a little harder at nine twenty. At nine twenty-five, cheered on by fellow queue members, he put his considerable full weight into trying to force the door. A slight cracking sound indicated the doorframe might be starting to give way. Then two police cars arrived, responding to the alarm set off at the police Station.

"Crikey, look at this, Phil!" spluttered Jill, at lunchtime that day. She pointed towards our new 26" Phillips TV. A very young-looking Mike Cross was smiling back at us from the screen, in full colour. "It's Mike, and that's from a wedding photo!"

"A postmaster has gone missing from a Solihull sub-post office this morning. £70,000 of benefits cash is also missing," announced Sharia Khan, the Central Region News midday newsreader… "Police are looking for the missing fifty-one-year-old postmaster, Mister Michael Cross, who has disappeared from the Hillfield post office at the same time as the cash. Foul play has not been ruled out. A large crowd of benefits claimants were left waiting outside the post office this morning, unable to cash their giro cheques." The announcer went on to say that all giros made out for payment at Hillfield could now be cashed at any West Midlands area post office.

"Poor Mike, it looks like he's had to 'do a runner'

with that cash!" said Jill.

"Yeah," I agreed, "I don't blame him, though, if that's what he's done. He was due to lose an absolute fortune when his shop loses its post office status next week. Let's hope he's okay."

We were astonished when Delia Cross entered The Miller's Arms a week later, on Thursday night and sat in the chair. THE Chair. The fireside chair that had become a permanent fixture and major attraction at the fifteenth century pub. Locals knew that this black plastic swivel chair was where you sat to tell a true story.

When Delia started her tale, she had the undivided attention of everyone in the pub. The bar staff stopped working and listened intently. No one was served while Delia recounted the hellish situation that she and Mike had landed in.

She recapped the story right from the start, telling all assembled about how the couple had invested the £38,000 from their house sale into buying the post office. Then how they stood to lose £19,000 when Susan Topping, the area's autocratic sub-post office regulator had declared that their shop's post office designation was cancelled. The fact that this one person had decided on this action. The audience was shocked to hear that such a respected organisation could act in this manner, through one 'Regulator'.

"So there we have it, we stood to lose all that money due to a decision made by this Susan Topping. She'd decided to close us down and thereby robbed me and Mike of a considerable sum. But it gets much worse…" Delia paused to sip a brandy kindly handed to her by Bill, the landlord.

"When Mike investigated, he was shocked to discover that another post office is planning to open right next door to our shop. The opening of this new shop exactly coincides with our closing date. The owner of this new shop is a current post office worker. The owner of this new shop is Susan bloody Topping. Yes, the very same 'Regulator', who'd poo-poo'd our twenty-three closely-vetted candidates, and ordered that our shop's post office status was terminated." As Delia looked around, she could read empathy written across all faces in the bar.

"Bloody scoundrel! This shouldn't be allowed in this day and age. Looks like this Susan Potting has shafted you and Mike, good 'n' proper. Buying a cheap shop next door, she'll double her money as soon as it becomes a post office! But what happened to Mike? He's missing, ain't he?" Chips, our resident Cockney taxi driver asked.

"Yes. Her name's 'Topping' by the way. Anyway, Mike decided there was no other option, he had to 'cut and run'. The security van delivered the £70,000 in cash at seven thirty a.m. as usual, last Thursday morning, ready for the giro pay-outs. Mike took the money and somehow — God knows how — he got to an airport. He rang me later that day from a country in southern Europe. No idea yet which one, he wouldn't say. He's safe and well. He sends his apologies to anyone put out by his action, but he had no choice. At least, in a way, we still have our investment. I wish it could have been done differently. We did try so hard to meet Post Office regulations. But when you have a back-stabber like this Regulator double crossing you and making money from our downfall…" she tailed off, dabbing her eyes with a tissue. "I've been very honest with the police, explaining everything I knew in detail." After finishing her drink, she said her 'goodnights' and left.

"Poor Delia," said Ivan the mechanic. "And Mike, you gotta feel for them, and I reckon given the same impossible situation, I'd have done exactly the same!"

All agreed with this sentiment. Delia continued drinking at 'The Milly' from time to time, especially on darts nights when she'd always update us with her latest news. "Mike flew from Coventry to Bilbao in Spain. He stayed there a couple of weeks then flew on to the Mediterranean island of Gozo, where he now lives," she informed us just before Christmas. "No extradition treaty currently exists between the UK and the Island, so he's fairly safe… for now. But he'd love to come home. Oh yes and I managed to sell the shop a month after closing, for twenty thousand pounds. So we would have been eighteen grand down."

It was five years later, after the 'hoo hah' had all died down, that Mike reappeared, one amazing night at our favourite pub. A Tuesday darts night, I recall.

At around eight thirty, the ex-postmaster entered the bar. I hugged my old chum and treated him to a pint of 'Yore Inn' best bitter. He made his way over to the fireplace and sat on The Story Teller's Chair, which had been recently reinstalled in its position, after being repaired by Ivan the mechanic.

The darts match took a break. The whole pub hushed. The duke box was unplugged. Nobody wanted to miss this.

"Hello you lot; it's good to be back!" Mike looked healthy and tanned but ten years older than the last time I'd seen him. Due to all the worry? A round of cheering and applause erupted.

"Good to see you again Mike! Did you have a good holiday?" Chips asked cheekily, to roars of laughter.

"The weather was an improvement on here." Mike sounded cheerful. "You probably all know about what happened to me and Delia, as a result of a crooked post office regulator?"

"Yes, Delia told us," said Jill. The crowd nodded.

"Well, I can now reveal that The post office seems to have relented on their pursuit of me. Possibly they realised that they, through the actions of their employee Susan Topping, were acting wrongfully. Any court case brought against me now would reveal the extent of damage the post office, through their rogue regulator, had inflicted on us. So, they're doing nothing. No apologies, mind. Just an unwritten truce."

"Anyway, there's just a few more details you don't know." The crowd hushed in anticipation.

"That fateful Thursday morning, the security van dropped off the £70,000 cash, in a bag, at around 7.30 a.m. I counted and signed for the money as usual. I then locked the shop up for the last time and stood outside on the pavement, in the rain, with the bag of money. Must admit I felt a bit vulnerable."

"After waiting for about five minutes, from out of

the drizzle, a long white Jaguar XJ6 saloon, with 'POLICE' in big blue letters written on the sides, pulled up beside me."

All eyes were agog in the bar. All breath was held.

"I opened the front passenger door and got in, clutching my sack of 'swag'. The driver, a tall, handsome young chap, in full police uniform, selected 'D' and floored the throttle. The big Jaguar launched smoothly forward, taking off rather like a jet aircraft. After a few streets the driver turned on the siren and blue lights. The car then cruised smoothly and effortlessly at breakneck speed through the streets of Solihull. Traffic parted as if by magic to allow us through. The car slowed only slightly when passing through red lights. We then sped along the A45, towards Coventry. The car was travelling so bloody fast on wet roads I had to ask the driver to ease off a bit. He did. The Jaguar police car pulled up at the Customs Shed at Coventry Airport barely seventeen minutes after picking me up."

"Before I got out, I kissed the police officer on the cheek and he handed me a suitcase from the back seat. As I strode off towards Customs with my suitcase and sackful of money I turned and said, 'Thanks, Son. One day I'll repay you for this'."

"Police Sergeant Neal Cross smiled, returned my wave and drove quietly away."

"Wow," said Ivan, "your lad Neal gave you the best lift ever! Those big Jags are great to drive by the way. I've got one."

"They're a bit heavy on juice though," observed his

mechanic pal Don. Chips nodded in agreement.

To the delight of all assembled, Mike rose from the chair, pulled out a wad of notes and declared, “All the drinks are on me tonight!”

And what a night! Jill and I were so glad that our old chums eventually achieved the redemption they truly deserved. I wonder if they ever visited the new Hillfield post office? I’ll ask them next time…

UPDATE: 34 years on:

Mike and Delia are living happily, in Warwick.

Detective Chief Superintendent Neal Cross lives happily with his wife and two children in the Midlands.

Susan Topping was dismissed from her position a few weeks after that fateful Thursday, when her employers realised the enormity of her actions.

Perhaps this 1980s case portended, for sub postmasters, the horrors of what was on the horizon?

From out of the drizzle, a long white Jaguar XJ6…

# Sand Which

The audience gathered round eagerly as I made myself comfortable in the old Story Teller's Chair in the fireplace of The Miller's Arms; almost, but not quite, in the fire! A cold winter's evening was always guaranteed to be productive. An audience of around twenty surrounded the chair as I began:

During the seventies I worked as a lorry driver for Austin Exhibitions. The company's headquarters were near the Royal Showground, at Stoneleigh in Warwickshire.

I would often be away on long-distance driving trips. As these jobs were presented to me at a moment's notice, my wife Jill kindly made sandwiches for me every day, so I'd always have something to eat, no matter where I was sent.

When not on these trips, I would sometimes lunch in the company's excellent subsidised canteen, leaving my wife's lovingly produced snack uneaten.

Now, if your missus makes you sandwiches, this is a very precious routine that you do not want to disrupt by taking uneaten sandwiches home. The provider might decide that their efforts were unappreciated, and probably end the service.

Not wishing this to happen, I became accustomed to the habit of disposing of any surplus sandwich 'evidence' before returning home, on the few days when I had lunched at the canteen. I generally ate at least one of the sandwiches at the morning tea break, though.

This happy state of affairs continued for some months; more often than not, the sandwiches, or most of them, were eaten. Any unconsumed were binned, prior to heading for home. Up until the day when it happened.

On the morning in question, there was an unusually high number of workers taking their ten o'clock break alongside me and my mate Ben in the woodwork shop. Painters, electricians, labourers, the foreman, and even the boss's son Roy had joined us. There were around thirty men assembled, sitting on various stools and benches, dotted around the workshop.

I didn't suspect anything at all. The company sometimes had meetings in this building, and as I had been off site for the last hour or so, I may have missed something.

I had. There had been conversations, and the subject was — me! I walked in, with my by now famous sandwich box, like a lamb to the slaughter…

As I cleared a space, sat down on a bench and opened my sandwiches, an eerie silence fell. Normally at this time, Jeff the carpenter would be giving out racing tips from a well-thumbed Racing Post, regaling us with the success of his latest fool-proof betting system. Curiously, he never mentioned any losses. Paul the foreman, who some unkind observers have noted would by now be a multi-millionaire if he was paid by the word, would be going over the details of the next big job, not missing the opportunity presented by a large captive audience. And Rick the labourer would be regaling us with another dirty joke. But not today… they all remained silent… even the radio had been turned down… It was as if they were waiting for something. Oh yes, they were bloody well waiting all right!

I hadn't realised it, but all eyes were on me. I opened my flask and poured myself a mug of tea, adding my customary four spoonfuls of sugar. I'd recently cut down from five spoons, too sweet! They were counting the stirs of my teaspoon. I always stir my tea for half a minute. The audience waited patiently, bless them!

Next, I opened a packet of crisps to go with my sandwiches.

I then extracted the cling-wrapped sandwiches from my lunchbox and carefully unravelled the film, to expose the neat, triangular-cut, delicious-looking feast. At this stage I was hungry with expectation; Would it be egg and tomato? cheese? fish? paste? fish paste? I never used to ask my wife what she was packing for me, preferring a surprise. Little did I know, but I was indeed in for a surprise that morning! I can imagine how a little earlier the jungle drums would have spread the word. "Be in the woodwork shed at ten o'clock, Phil's going to bite off more than he can chew! Heh, heh!"

Suspense would have built even more, as at that point I took a sip of tea.

Then, at last, I did what they were all waiting for; I lifted the first sandwich and put the un-crusted, pointed portion into my mouth. I expected my teeth to sink clear through the sandwich. They did not. Instead, they met something very hard in the middle. I knew we were economising, but I'd never had meat quite this tough, I thought.

I spat the sandwich filling onto the floor in disgust. "What the…" my words trailed off in disbelief.

Old George the painter leapt off the bench and gleefully sprinted over and picked it up. I'd never seen him move so fast. He picked up a triangular-shaped piece of cardboard and we could all see some thick, black, felt-tip lettering on it.

"Well, I never," he squealed with delight, "what on earth are you eating these days Phil, cardboard?" At this, the audience started tittering.

"Something my dearly beloved fashioned for me on the cheap, I suspect George. What does that writing say?"

"It says 'HONEY ROAST HAM, CANTEEN STYLE'," replied George, to widespread guffaws of laughter. The whole assemblage had, by now, descended into uncontrollable spasms of hysteria. Ian the foreman carpenter fell off his perch, high up on a window sill and severely injured his left arm. Even in extreme pain, he could not stop laughing. An ambulance was summoned.

The lads gathered round me in gleeful expectation as I unwrapped the other three sandwiches and dissected them. They each contained a similar triangle of cardboard, cunningly glued into the bread with a smear of butter.

I read the thick, black, felt-tip capital titles, proclaiming three exotic varieties:

'CRAYFISH SALAD, CANTEEN STYLE'

'ROAST VENISON, CANTEEN STYLE'

I don't understand it..." I turned them over, in the vain hope of finding a morsel to eat.

"I reckon you're a very lucky man, Phil. I never get sandwiches with tasty fillings like that!" remarked Paul the foreman, to another round of laughter.

"Well, neither do I...especially not today!" I countered. "I'd have settled for door-stop cheese today, rather than this..."

"Perhaps your missus thinks you need more fibre!" chipped in Roy.

"She's getting her own back," said Ben, knowingly. "Maybe she found out about those sarnies you sometimes throw away when you've eaten at the canteen?"

Ginger the apprentice found a short piece of bent wire embedded in one of the cards. "Obviously part of your 'staple diet'!" he suggested. Ian groaned in genuine agony, still on the floor where he had landed, trying not to laugh. A rolled-up overall had been placed under his head for comfort.

The ambulance arrived ten minutes later to take the foreman carpenter to hospital. We could still hear him chuckling and gasping in equal measures of hysteria and pain after the doors had closed and the vehicle pulled away. He was off work for two weeks.

By the time I got home and accosted Jill about this, my temper had abated. She rightly argued that if the sandwiches had been dumped, as they sometimes were, firstly I would not have even known about the cardboard contents, and secondly, a useful economy would have been achieved. She was right.

I did see the humorous side eventually and learned a lesson. Never again would I throw good food away. The consequences are far too embarrassing, wasteful and even dangerous! Jill has never divulged her source of intelligence regarding the matter. I have my suspicions. Non-cardboard sandwich fillings, were resumed. All were eaten.

A welcome round of applause from the barflies rewarded my revelation.

"Good one, Phil! I take it you could manage some Miller's style beer?" invited my old pal, Ivan.

"You bet I could, cheers!" I said.

"Never waste food mate, there's millions starving in this world at this very moment." Chips, our very own Cockney taxi driver, as usual, had the last word.

Then I did what they were all waiting for…

# Unit Wit

The usual cronies were huddled around the log fire in the parlour bar that cold, October evening when my pal Ivan, a very tall, jovial, balding mechanic joined us.

Ivan was a 'regular' at The Miller's Arms; about twice a week he would grace us with his presence. Not quite a 'Crony', to earn that title you would need to be here on parade at least five times a week and to have bequeathed your liver to science.

No slave to fashion, dressed in his usual 'double denim', Ivan sauntered over with his pint towards the fireplace and sat in the only empty chair. THE Chair.

"Story, story, story!" chanted the assemblage in unison. Ivan looked startled at first when he noticed the chant was directed at him. Then it dawned on him. He was fully aware that traditionally, this chair was sat in only on the condition that the occupier told a story. Not just any story either; it had to be true, and preferably humorous.

Ivan obliged with this nugget about a motor trade acquaintance.

"So you want a true, humorous story, eh? Okay, here is one about my old mate Don and his wife, Muriel. He is quite a character; how shall I put it, a lovable rogue? A sort of a cross between 'Del Boy Trotter' and 'Sergeant Bilko', if you can imagine such a man! A mechanic by trade, but he has many other strings to his bow!"

Indeed, Bilko or Del Boy would have been very proud of the way Don and his wife Muriel schemed to pull the wool over the eyes of a security officer from a major bank…

A fifty-year-old chap, of average height and with a mousey, slightly greying, comb-over hairstyle, Don was always dabbling in various 'business opportunities'. Whenever a moneymaking scheme came his way, he jumped in with both feet. The trouble is, sometimes you need to 'look before you leap'!

On this occasion he'd bought a three-year-old white Transit van, for no other reason than because it was going so damn cheap, he just couldn't resist it.

Now, he'd thought, what was the best way to turn that van into a 'nice little earner'?

After much pondering and deliberation, Don decided he would set up in business as a courier.

"What about D & M Courier Services?" asked Don's wife, Muriel, between mouthfuls of cereal over the breakfast table. She was slightly shorter than Don, two years younger and a tad wider. She'd often say 'I've still got what I had twenty years ago, it's all just a little bit lower, that's all!'

"'D & M Courier Services UK Ltd.' sounds bigger." Don muffled his reply through a bacon and egg banjo and between the pages of The Times.

Most of this paper's content went straight over

Don's head, much like his hairstyle. But he had thought that it looked the part, it was a proper businessman's paper. A paper you could leave lying around to impress visitors. The newsagent had been most surprised, shocked even, when Don cancelled 'The Sport' in favour of the highbrow broadsheet.

"Oh yes, 'D & M Courier Services UK Ltd' it is," agreed Muriel, between sips of delicious Camp coffee. And so another venture was born. "I'll get some letterheads and leaflets designed and printed." She was a very good partner in all ways to Don; over the years they had started up more businesses than Richard Branson; closed them as well, mind. The pair were on a par with each other.

An early potential customer for them turned out to be a major high street bank. The bank made contact on the day they'd received D & M's flashy brochure in the post.

Muriel took the phone call, answering in what she thought was a very posh voice. "D & M Courier Services, UK. Muriel speaking, how can I help you?" She emphasised the 'UK' as if it was a department of a much larger operation.

"Good afternoon, Muriel, my name is Bertha Strong, and I'm calling from Berkley's Bank. We received your brochure and price list this morning and wonder if your company can help with transport and storage of the bank's valuable and promotional items?" Bertha asked.

"Yes, we'll be happy to help, if we can..." Whilst talking, Muriel deftly herded Alan the Rottweiler through a door and into the garage.

Details were exchanged, and Bertha then announced, “We would like to discuss the possibility of D & M acting for Berkley’s Bank in principle, on condition that your premises are suitable and secure. Could we arrange a site visit for our head of security to inspect your offices and storage facilities please?”

This was a simple request, but... oh dear, there was just a very slight problem. ‘D & M Courier Services UK Ltd’ did not have any business premises. Working from their semi-detached house on a Warwick housing estate and storing parcels in the garage was the business plan. This would save hugely on overheads; but obviously may not suit the bank.

“Yes, of course, we’d be happy to arrange a visit to our offices and storage facility,” replied Muriel, thinking quickly. “I’ll have to ring you back to arrange an appointment though, as I’d like to make sure our C.E.O., Mr Don Randall, is available to meet your manager and show him around personally. I’ll call you back within a couple of days if that’s okay?” Bertha said it was and Muriel broke out into a sweat as she ended the call.

Don scratched his head and raked his comb-over when he heard the news. “That’s good so far, but we’ll need to come up with a plan for the meeting,” he declared.

What could they do? Rent a business unit? No. They dismissed that straight away; too expensive. Such a luxury would eat into their profits! Could they convert their house? No, too much work. Then Don had an idea.

Frantically he searched the 'Business Premises to Let' pages in The Warwick Morning Express. Soon he found what he was looking for:

**'Secure Business Units to let, from 1,000 square feet. Warwick area…'**

The number answered on the second ring. "Acme Business Lettings, good morning. Brian speaking, how can I help you?"

"I do hope you can help me, Brian, I'm looking for business premises…" Don went on to detail the size and type of unit that would suit, i.e., look good from the bank's point of view.

"What luck, we have one available on an industrial estate in Warwick that should fit the bill, would you like to view it?" asked Brian.

A meeting was arranged and Don was shown around the medium-sized business unit, just off Harbury Lane the next day.

The unit had 2,000 square feet of storage space behind a stout-looking roller shutter door. Adjacent to this was the reception and an office. Just what the bank would expect, thought Don.

"I think this unit may be suitable for our purposes, but I'd like to invite my business advisor round for a private viewing, before I make a final decision. Can you let me have the keys for a few hours one day next week please Brian?" pleaded Don, hopefully.

"Of course, just collect them from my office on the day you want them," smiled the agent. "Anything to oblige a potential tenant!" Brian beamed. Acme Business Lettings, like a lot of firms in the early nineties was going through hard times. I dare say that if Don had asked Brian to provide a formation display team of blindfolded juggling unicyclists to perform at the unit on that day, it would have been a wish granted.

Gleefully, Don arranged an appointment for the bank's security officer to inspect 'D & M's' premises on the following Tuesday. But there was some frantic cosmetic work to be done in the meantime, if the ruse was going to work. First stop was the local sign writer's shop.

On Tuesday morning, after collecting the unit keys from Brian, Dennis and Muriel drove the Transit van first to the local cardboard box factory, where they bought a large selection of 'end of run' boxes. Then they made their way to the local refuse tip and recycling centre. Various bits and pieces of obsolete office equipment and furniture were selected from the piles of detritus and added to the van-load of props and paraphernalia.

"Doesn't matter if it works or not…" Don began…

"…so long as it looks okay." Muriel finished the sentence for him, whilst spinning round on an office chair. Soon they set off for the unit, fully laden with their haul.

Within an hour of their arrival, the unit had been transformed. The building looked exactly what you'd expect for a busy logistics company. The 'Acme Business Letting's 'TO LET' board had been overlaid with a new sign, pronouncing:

**'D & M COURIER SERVICES UK Ltd. HEADQUARTERS.'**

Defunct computers, permanently-locked, keyless filing cabinets and rubber plants rescued from a skip were placed strategically throughout the building. A large quantity of empty cardboard boxes were stacked on shelving in the main storage area. 'Health & Safety at Work' notices, empty fire extinguishers, 'FIRE EXIT' signs and even a first aid box were all in position ready for the ten-thirty appointment.

Don carefully taped up the loose ends of telephone wires - which led nowhere - to a leg of the receptionist's desk.

"Don't forget to keep talking on them phones Babe, we don't want him asking to make a call do we? Look busy!" Don reminded his wife. "I wish talking was an Olympic sport, you'd be a bloody gold medal winner!" He ducked a friendly swipe.

Muriel rammed another fistful of red marker pins into the huge map of the British Isles hung on the wall behind the receptionist's desk.

She had overdone the pins though, decided Don; he pulled a few out so that you could at least make out the familiar coastline, confirming that it was indeed a map of the British Isles, and not some strange example of 'modern art'.

A rescued fax machine was 'dressed up', with a roll of spurious 'orders' which Muriel had typed laboriously the previous night, apparently spewing out of it in profusion. This placed in a corner of reception was the finishing touch.

Soon the pair were poised to perform an elaborate charade of deception.

At ten thirty, the bank's representative entered the building on time and introduced himself to reception. Smiling so much her jaw ached, Muriel held the handset of a dead intercom to her mouth and shouted rather loudly, "Mr Richard Head of Berkley's Bank to see you, Sir."

Don heard his wife clearly enough, having had his ear firmly pressed to the office door. He sprinted to his seat behind the desk, smoothed down his comb-over and tried to look relaxed. Just in time he remembered to wipe the excess Brylcream off his right hand and carefully placed 'The Financial Times' where it could not be missed.

"Would you like to go through? Mr Randall will see you now, sir." Muriel indicated the door marked **'D. RANDALL BSc CEng Chief Executive Officer**'. These qualifications were a slight exaggeration, though. Don had left school at the age of fifteen, with nothing but a worn-out satchel.

Don looked up from behind the huge pile of pretend paperwork snaffled from a recycling skip as the man from the bank knocked and entered. "Mr Head? Don Randall, very pleased to meet you," he beamed. The two men squeezed the blood from each other's hands and looked each other squarely in the eye. Mr Head was a few inches taller than Don but both were dressed smartly in dark grey suits with all the trimmings. Don always kept his jacket undone, though, to accommodate a well-developed beer belly.

"Please, call me Dick," invited the banker, flexing his fingers and finding them surprisingly slippery.

"And I'm Don, please do take a seat, Dick," the CEO pointed to the guest's seat and the bank's security and logistics executive officer duly sat on a black plastic swivel chair. Earlier that day, this chair had been thrown away by a local dog trainer as it had been badly chewed at the back. Muriel had managed to patch over this hole using large pieces of what she called 'insulting tape'.

After a couple of minutes of the usual courtesy exchanges and small talk, there was a knock at the door.

"Sorry to interrupt you, sir, but Nigel in van number six just rang from Northern Ireland; the ferry has been delayed so he won't be able to make his timed pick-up, at the jeweller's in Liverpool," said Muriel breathlessly.

"Okay, get Gordon in van four to make the jewellery collection on his way back from Carlisle. Would you like a coffee, Dick?" asked Don slickly; hoping Dick had not noticed the heavily rehearsed nature of the duo's last exchange.

"Yes, white with one sugar, please," Dick smiled at Muriel, who returned it sweetly as she swept efficiently from the office. "You seem to be very busy," he remarked to Don, but it was also a question.

"Oh, yes, non-stop!" Don lied through his teeth. "Luckily, we have enough vans to cover any unforeseen hitches. The main thing for us is to keep our customers happy and meet their deadlines. Now, first things first, would you like to see our storage facilities, Dick?"

Dick nodded and Don rose from his seat, turned and

walked over to the back of the office and attempted to open the door in that wall. The handle turned but the door remained firmly shut. He tried again, more vigorously, but there was no movement. It was locked. "Bugger!" he gasped inadvertently. This is all I need, thought Don.

"Pardon?" asked Mr Head, as he peered curiously over Don's shoulder.

Luckily, thinking on his feet was instinctive for Don. "Oh, of course, I remember now. Our security advisor has asked us to always keep this door locked," he explained, hopefully convincingly.

"This way," Don escorted the visitor back through reception where Muriel was giving an Oscar-winning performance. She had one phone trapped between her left shoulder and her jaw, and another phone in her right hand.

"Can you give me the weight, in kilograms, of each package and the delivery address postcodes? Will you hold, please?" she asked her shoulder.

Then she barked to the phone in her right hand, "Your account, Mr Hughes, invoice number three two zero nine. The total amount is two thousand, one hundred and three pounds, seventy-six pence, including V.A.T."... theatrical pause... "Yes, please, if you could make it payable to D & M Courier Services UK Ltd. Thank you."

She caught Don's eye and her free left hand gesticulated towards the two steaming mugs of Camp coffee on her desk. She had just poured these from the thermos flask, which was now hidden behind her chair.

Don passed one mug to Dick and took the other for himself. Don grimaced. This tasted like poison to him; white with one sugar! He hadn't had sugar or milk for over thirty years! Aargh! But needs must…

"Delicious coffee," remarked Dick, as he sipped his drink appreciatively.

The two men carried their drinks through a door marked 'Storage Area', as an unlettered white Renault Trafic van drew up. The driver entered the building and pulled on a long chain to raise the roller-shutter door. "G'mornin' Mr Randall," smiled the middle-aged slim ginger haired man. Don was pleased to note that he was dressed in plain white overalls.

"Morning Len, how did that London trip go?" asked Don. He was glad to see his old pal Len, a plumber, was there on time. In The Top Lock Inn last night he had asked a couple of his plain white van owning friends to pop round to the unit and do a bit of play acting at various times throughout the morning. Bob the painter was due to turn up around eleven o'clock.

"It was fine thanks, the M40 was fairly clear this morning!" smiled Len with a twinkle in his eye. Don had promised him twenty quid for this performance. Len proceeded to load ten of the empty cardboard boxes into the back of his van, grunting and bending to create the illusion of great weight. Don hoped Len's overacting hadn't been detected.

"Right, that's Wednesday's Glasgow trip loaded. See you tomorrow, Don!" Len winked at Don before driving off with a huge grin on his face.

Don waved a 'goodbye' to Len and proceeded to

proudly escort his guest on a tour of the loading bay. The shelves were filled with cardboard boxes festooned with a variety of spurious address labels, proclaiming: **'NEW YORK, SYDNEY, CAPE TOWN, SINGAPORE, HONOLULU, BUENOS AIRES, BEIJING, REDDITCH'** etcetera as optimistic and rather exotic destinations. Had Mr Head thought to pick up one of the boxes he would have been astonished to discover just how light they were.

When the two men re-entered reception, the talented telephonist was this time apparently explaining D & M's high security policy to a prospective client. "Yes, we only use plain, unlettered vans, and we use a box number for our company address; we don't want to draw undue attention as we handle very valuable items…"

She continued talking after the men had returned to Don's office and the door had closed. "Cats and dogs, rhubarb, rhubarb, cats and dogs…" she mumbled, a technique she had learnt as a child whilst performing background crowd scenes in school plays.

"I must say, I am very impressed indeed with the set-up you have here at D & M Courier Services," said Mr Head as he drained his mug and prepared to leave. "Especially by your attitude to security, this is essential for us at Berkley's Bank. Here is the draft contract for your scrutiny. I'm pleased to say that I'll be recommending to my colleagues that we do business with your company, Don. That is… if you can fit us in?" The Bank's Logistics Manager smiled warmly as he handed the paperwork to a delighted Don.

Mr Head saw Bob the painter's brand-new white

VW Transporter van reversing up to the roller shutter door, just as he was leaving D & M's 'Headquarters'. Dick waved. Bob smiled and waved back. Twenty quid for a wave, he thought. Bloody bargain!

Later that day, as he handed the unit keys back to a very disappointed Brian at the lettings agents, Don explained that sorry, his business advisor had said that the unit was not large enough after all, thank you and yes please, keep him posted if a bigger unit became available. Brian was deflated to say the least.

The lucrative contract to provide courier services for Berkley's Bank was signed two days later. Don and Muriel celebrated with a huge party.

I can assure you that for seven years during the 1990s, Berkley's Bank's most highly sensitive files and valuable packages were stored very securely. At Don and Muriel's semi-detached house. On the Wedgenock housing estate, in Warwick. In the garage. In battered old tea crates. Between the washing machine and Alan the Rottweiler's kennel.

"Well told, Ivan, I bet you could manage a pint?" I strolled over to the bar amidst a round of applause. "Two pints of 'Yore Inn' please, Kaz." The landlady smiled as she pulled the golden coloured ales.

Chips chipped in. "We know Don and Muriel quite well, they drink here sometimes. They ain't bad sorts. Salts o' the earth. By the way, I think it was Don who donated that very chair you're sittin' on, Ivan!"

We looked at the chair. It was a black, plastic, swivelling type. There was a large insulation taped patch on the back.

Muriel was giving an Oscar-winning performance.